# The Gift c

*Living with my Husband and Di*

## By the Revd Canon Pat Prestney
*with Ivan Sage*

*Mercy holds the veil that hides tomorrow*

'Does Keith see things?' the consultant enquired. 'Does he have hallucinations?'

'Yes,' I replied.

'Does he still dress himself?'

'Yes.'

'Can he go to the loo by himself?'

'Yes.'

. . . and then he asked: 'Has he tried to kill you yet?'

*Dedicated to the memory of Keith Prestney, a gentle man, and to all who are living with Diffuse Lewy Body Disease, and to those who care for them.*

First published independently in 2013
by the Revd Canon Pat Prestney, 2 Cedar Way, Great Bentley,
Colchester, Essex: 01206 255319

Printed by Alphaprint (Colchester) Ltd, Essex

All profits made from the sale of this book will be donated to
Diffuse Lewy Bodies Disease research

ISBN-13: 978-0-9926007-0-9

# INDEX

|  | INTRODUCTION | P6 |
| Chapter 1 | LOVE AT FIRST SIGHT | P10 |
| Chapter 2 | DIRE STRAIGHTS | P19 |
| Chapter 3 | A SHOCKING DIAGNOSIS | P31 |
| Chapter 4 | A GATHERING STORM | P43 |
| Chapter 5 | A MIRACLE – AND SCARY CUSHIONS! | P56 |
| Chapter 6 | THE BUBBLE BURSTS | P84 |
| Chapter 7 | A LONELY PLACE | P93 |
| Chapter 8 | A POSSIBLE CAUSE? | P102 |
| Chapter 9 | KEITH – IN HIS OWN WORDS | P108 |
| Chapter 10 | HELP IS OUT THERE | P121 |
| Chapter 11 | THE IMPORTANCE OF FAMILY | P139 |
| Chapter 12 | DEEPEST LOVE | P147 |
| Chapter 13 | A SCARE AND MAGICAL MOMENTS | P155 |
| Chapter 14 | A PEACEFUL FAREWELL | P170 |
| Chapter 15 | 'GRANDPA'S GOODBYE PARTY' | P176 |
| Chapter 16 | MOVING ON | P180 |
|  | USEFUL CONTACTS | P185 |
|  | USEFUL INFORMATION | P188 |
|  | ACKNOWLEDGEMENTS | P189 |

# INTRODUCTION

## By Ivan Sage

Keith Robert Prestney died just short of his 76th birthday on 2 May, 2010. Prior to his death his wife Pat and I had begun writing this book to document his 11-year struggle for survival against overwhelming odds. His untimely passing, however, does not in any way diminish the story of the remarkable resilience he and his family displayed over so many years because the end was so inevitable.

So, why do I describe Keith's death as 'untimely'? Simply because, according to so many consultants and doctors, Keith was widely expected to succumb to his illness several years earlier.

By picking up this book you have just selected a remarkable and inspiring love story – but make no mistake, this is not a slushy Mills & Boon novel. No, this is a tale of real life devotion and commitment in an imperfect world – an inspiring tale that demonstrates how love had no boundaries and no hurdle was too high to overcome. It also reveals the hard facts of life that can be encountered when life leads you down a particularly difficult and emotionally challenging path.

This is the story of Pat and Keith Prestney. Prepare to be moved and inspired by this remarkable couple – a couple I have been both proud and privileged to know as friends. Their experiences will have you either smiling or close to tears as the rollercoaster of their lives over the past few traumatic years unravels from page to page.

When I first met Keith no-one knew that he was on the cusp of a cruel, debilitating disease that would turn his and his family's lives upside down.

To my mind, Keith was not only a gentleman but a *gentle man* whose benevolent manner made him instantly endearing to anyone fortunate enough to meet him. His wife Pat, the rector of the small Essex village where we all lived, shared Keith's qualities and it's hard to imagine how a couple could have been more suited and devoted to each other.

Keith had been a hard working, fit and active man with a keen sense of fun for the first 64 years of his life. Then, in 1998, Pat noticed that his usual spark was missing. He began to slow down dramatically as both his mobility and mental health deteriorated. Confusion and mobility difficulties became more and more apparent before their lives were turned upside down with the diagnosis of Diffuse Lewy Body Disease. Keith, they were informed, would be unlikely to survive more than the next two to three years.

Like most people, the Prestneys had never heard of this awful, debilitating and degenerative disease which shares similar symptoms to Parkinson's Disease, but which progresses far more ruthlessly. Remarkably, given that so many people claim never to have heard of Diffuse Lewy Body Disease, it is one of most common forms of dementia. Sadly, there is no cure.

What makes this particular story stand out is an amazing 'window of opportunity' that occurred after Keith's condition had become so dire that he was barely able to communicate in any way or care for himself. Circumstances and an experimental cocktail of medication conspired to offer the Prestneys a period of time where Keith, almost overnight, emerged from his mysterious parallel world like a butterfly from a chrysalis, almost back to his former self.

This 'small miracle of science' enabled Keith to describe the feelings and fears he had experienced while being unable to communicate with his family and to enjoy his family, his home and even holidays abroad.

This is truly the uplifting part of this incredible tale which we very much hope will give encouragement to anyone caring for someone who is unable to communicate as a result of their condition.

Unfortunately, Keith's recovery was too good to last and, over time, his condition began to deteriorate once more. Yet the struggle to offer him a reasonable standard of life continued unabated. Eleven years on from his diagnosis, and despite several scares along the way, Keith was still sharing his home with his beloved wife.

Despite the considerable difficulties he faced in life, he was still able to enjoy the company of his three sons, their wives and his grandchildren.

This, according to most medical theories, just shouldn't have been possible but Pat is convinced Keith's life was prolonged and enhanced by the level of care she, their family, medics and carers had been able to bestow upon him.

Pat, in her former capacity as the village priest, certainly knows the value of life, but she also appreciates the importance attached to a decent quality of life – not only for sufferers but for their carers too. Despite so much heartache along the way this is, nevertheless, an uplifting story of faith, love, hope and determination.

This is not intended to be an authoritative account of the effects of Diffuse Lewy Body Disease. Far from it. This is a very personal account of how the disease affected not only Keith, but his entire family; it's about how they came to terms with it; and how they and others coped with it (or not, at times).

This is *their* story. A story which begins back when Keith was a schoolboy and traces his life from there on. We discover the type of man he was, his aims, his work, his dreams – basically the man he was before this cruel disease changed his life irrevocably. Only by learning what Keith was like prior to his illness can one truly appreciate how vastly life changed for him and his family after his diagnosis.

What happened to Keith when he emerged from a position of not being able to communicate with others may well have been a one-off but that 'window of opportunity' when, seemingly against all the odds, he became lucid once more, offers a rare insight into a twilight world that few would ever expect to understand.

Although this story of Keith's re-emergence to a fully conscious and mobile state is remarkable, the feelings, fears and thoughts he was able to express will, hopefully, not only enlighten but uplift those caring for loved ones who are totally unable to communicate with them.

Looking after someone who seems to be locked in to a world of their own, not knowing what they are thinking, feeling, wanting or understanding, is a painful and heart-rending process but Pat and Keith's experiences will shed some light on the dark times so many people have to endure.

Perhaps this story will, to some degree, reassure carers of those who seem to be locked deeply in a world of their own that their loved ones can, most likely, hear and understand what is being said and done around them and that their efforts can be appreciated even if the person being cared for is not in a position to express it personally.

Sadly, there is no happy ending to this story but Keith's life was undeniably extended considerably and was made far more bearable by the dedicated efforts of a marvellous consultant and Keith's devoted family and carers so, in that sense, it is a story of what may be possible for others.

I hope this devoted family's story may inspire you as much as it has me.

# LOVE AT FIRST SIGHT

The consultant didn't pull any punches. He looked directly at me. 'How old is Keith?' he asked. 'He's 67,' I replied. 'Well,' he said, 'he might make 70, but it'll probably be best if he doesn't.'

Almost nine years later, as I gazed across the lounge at my dear husband sitting quietly in his chair in our lounge I realised he was but a shadow of the man I met and fell in love with. It was so hard to believe that this frail gentleman who I shared my life with, the man I loved so deeply, had become so physically and mentally challenged that he required the help of myself and carers to tend to his everyday needs. How I wished I could turn back the clock to the days when he was able to enjoy each day as it came. How I wished I could have done something to help him escape from the clutches of the cruel, killer disease that had been blighting his life since it was diagnosed in 1999. But then again, I thanked God I still had the man who had confounded the medics who believed he would be unlikely to survive more than two or three years.

It was the summer of 1967 and I was just 17 when I first met Keith. I was still at school and Keith often popped in to my father's transport café in the Essex village of Little Bentley for his lunch – but I reckon that was probably only because he fancied my friend! Keith would bring his strawberries to the café to be sold. He always looked rather scruffy and would appear in a battered old Mini. At first I only knew Keith as The Strawberry Man. My friend Jane and I used to wear short shorts, part of the Shell petroleum uniform, with a blue top and a little hat – and I think Keith really liked that! Jane and I had been working at the café over that summer and, as Keith appeared more and more often, we got to know him and he became a good friend who would often hang around for a chat with us.

At the time Keith and I were both going out with other people but, at the end of that strawberry season, Keith announced that he would like to take Jane and me out for dinner by way of a thank-you for selling his strawberries. Jane reckoned her mother wouldn't approve but I thought I'd really like to go, even though my dad wasn't so keen on the idea. I'm so glad I went. Keith turned up looking absolutely gorgeous in a red AC Ace sports car. Looking on, Jane must have been thinking she'd made a big mistake but it was too late. I hopped in to Keith's car and he drove us to the Red Lion pub in nearby Kirby where we had a wonderful time.

When I came home I told a friend, 'I'm going to marry that man!' I later ended my relationship with my boyfriend, Keith split with his girlfriend, and we became an item. My ex-boyfriend eventually went off to work in London. I never actually met Keith's girlfriend. I liked to think she wasn't very nice, though the opposite is probably true but, having met each other, Keith and I just knew we wanted to be together. Keith was blessed with a great sense of humour and that was probably the main aspect of his character that attracted me to him. We'd spend so much time laughing at things together.

Shortly afterwards Keith turned up to help set up my 18th birthday party at my parents' home which was adjacent to the café. That's when he first met most of my friends. Like me, they were considerably younger than Keith who was 33 years old at the time. To be honest, I'd had no idea he was so much older than me, I'd guessed he was probably in his twenties, but he'd won me over with his blue eyes and his lovely sense of humour. He was such a lovely person to talk to and we just clicked. I was instantly smitten. I knew Keith fancied me, but it still took him a full two years before he realised he wanted to marry me!

However, the path of true love rarely runs smoothly and, when I took up a nursing position in 1968 at Addenbrookes Hospital in Cambridge, Keith and I nearly split up. Keith had to remain at Greshams, the fruit farm he owned and ran in the small village of Great Bromley, and he was also working at another farm he rented in nearby Weeley while I was working miles away in Cambridgeshire. Greshams was originally just an empty field. When Keith took it on he grew strawberries and roses and then he was granted planning permission to build a farm house.

At the time we met, Keith was having the foundations of his own house, a chalet bungalow based on an Ideal Home design, laid down at Greshams. Keith had started building Greshams in 1966. I used to joke that although he'd got the foundations down he'd need a wife to build the walls. Time was of the essence. Although Keith was doing a lot of the building work himself, it was necessary to get the roof in situ by a certain date in order to avoid the need to pay a considerable amount in stamp duty.

Sport was Keith's passion, he loved it. He played fly half at rugby but he was not at all stocky. He was never a heavy man, he was more wiry. When he played hockey spectators often likened him to a little terrier – head down and onwards – and that was one of Keith's characteristics. He was a very good hockey player, a very good team player who was quite content to supply the passes for others to score whenever the opportunity arose. He captained Iceni, a Colchester-based hockey team, and represented both Essex and Suffolk at the sport. He also enjoyed playing cricket each summer – at least until his work commitments curtailed his participation.

Keith loved holidays, especially going abroad. A year after we started going out – I was 19 at the time – we went to Majorca, a holiday that wasn't exactly without incident as I couldn't find my passport – Keith, it turned out, had it all the time! Life was so different back then. We had separate rooms, on the insistence of my parents, who must have been concerned about their teenage daughter going on holiday with an older man. However, Keith was very shy, very reserved and courteous in a very old-fashioned way. He wouldn't have thought of going against my father's wishes. When my father asked if we had booked separate rooms, Keith would never have said 'yes' and not been truthful about it. I guess it was just a different era to today. Youngsters today would probably just laugh at how innocent we were.

I suppose it was inevitable that the distance between us caused by me working in Cambridge and Keith in Essex would put a strain on our relationship but, in spite of that, when I was 19 in September 1969, love won through and we became engaged. Three months later I finished my work at Addenbrookes and we were married on a very cold, snowy day on January 31, 1970 at Little Bentley church which was just up the road from Greshams. We had ushers who were all tall, much taller than Keith and I. They were wearing big coats but, as it was so cold, they were all hunched up and it looked like we were surrounded by Mafia henchmen!

We honeymooned in Portugal and then I transferred to the main hospital in Colchester where I worked for six months, but I gave up on my nursing training when the combination of working on Greshams and working night shifts all became a bit too much. After our marriage I'd moved into Keith's third floor flat in Inglis Road, Colchester. Meanwhile, we both worked hard at getting Greshams ready to move into. Then, in July 1970, I returned to work, this time at a dental practice in Colchester.

We eventually moved in to Greshams, in July 1971. Keith's parents had already moved into a house on the other side of the road. Keith's father was an absolute darling. His mother was more like me so I guess we tended to clash a little, but she was one of a kind, such a character, I've never met anyone else like her. I think she thought at one point they were going to move in to the house at Greshams when it was built but, in the meantime, Keith had met me and that plan never came to fruition.

Nevertheless, Keith's mother and I eventually became very good, close friends. Having them across the road was tremendous, particularly as Keith was very close to both his parents. We would both have tea in bed, have our breakfast and then Keith would go across the road every morning to visit his parents for half an hour, and he'd go back again at the end of the day for a while before we sat down for our tea.

Life was quite exciting. The time we spent transforming the house into a home was a lovely period in our lives. I didn't want to move in until we had a reasonable kitchen, somewhere to sit in the evenings, a bedroom and a bathroom. However, when we first moved in, it was still pretty basic. Keith worked so hard – particularly bearing in mind how much work he had to do on the farm. Although the builders had put up the walls, the windows and the roof, Keith and I did most of the other work.

When we were first married, the floor of the lounge/dining room – which was huge – was completely bare, an earth floor. We bought a second-hand oak floor which was covered in linoleum, from the garrison at Colchester. We laid it down and scraped off all the linoleum, then polished it up which was well worth the effort as a beautiful oak parquet flooring was revealed. It was lovely to do that together, even though it was jolly hard work. We had a friend called Sid who was in the building trade who helped out from time to time. He was the boss. For our part, I guess Keith and I were the lads, doing as Sid was instructing us along the way. Someone else plastered the walls, otherwise, I think we did just about everything else.

Life was pretty good and Keith and I, despite being quite different in our own ways, got on wonderfully well. Keith was always very quiet. He would never be the one who would say 'Come on, let's go down the pub', or 'let's go to the theatre', but if ever I suggested we went to a pub or to the theatre, he'd love it. If ever I suggested we have people round for dinner he'd say: 'Oh, no, not tonight', but, whenever people came, he'd be the perfect host.

I suppose Keith's idea of an ideal life would have been to enjoy a quiet time at home with his family, just enjoying himself with us. I know some people, when they first met Keith, may have thought he was very reserved, but he was so witty and clever. It's not as though he was ever unambitious, just that he'd never been one to draw attention to himself. He absolutely hated being in the spotlight.

Despite keeping ourselves busy we still found time to indulge in our passion for holidays. We went on a cruise around the Mediterranean which included a three-day visit to Israel and, later, we went to Morocco – which turned out to be the last holiday we'd enjoy together before our children were born. Before the boys came along I'd help Keith on the farm. Was Keith my boss? Well, he would have liked to think so! I have to admit I was a lousy farmer's wife, never very good at it. On the other hand, Keith was an extremely good farmer. It was his passion, even though he'd had no background in farming.

When Keith was a small child he was sent away to Dames' School, which he absolutely hated. His one pleasure there, however, was his window box in which he'd cultivate seeds and that instigated his passion for growing. I suppose Keith's father should have been a grower of some sort because he was very good at it. Later in life Keith went to school at a public boarding school in Holt, Norfolk called Greshams, a period of his life that he truly loved, and that's why, later in life, he decided to name his own farm after the school he had so much affection for.

Keith went on to attend Writtle Horticultural College as a young man. He really enjoyed it there, it was a good time in his life, and then, when he was 20, he did his two years' National Service, working in an office at Aldershot where the officers were trained. However, Keith didn't really enjoy Army life, although he did enjoy the comradeship. Then he went to work in Bury for a while where he learned how to be a horticulturalist at a rose growers.

He then began growing his own roses in two fields near Colchester and began supplying a local company, Cant's, who specialised in roses. It was arduous work, but Keith put his back into it to make it a success. He then began to grow strawberries and apple trees and that's around the time I first knew him.

When I'd finished full time work I'd help Keith plant out the strawberries and help out when it was time to pick them. Day-to-day life involved hard work on the farm during the daytime and working on the house at Greshams in the evenings. It was good fun, but such hard work. Although it was very tiring, Keith was tremendous. What stamina he had! I've never known anyone able to keep going as long as he did. He had tremendous inner strength as well as outer strength. Maybe that's what kept him going for so long when he became ill.

Physically he could work and work and work. I'll never know where he got his energy from. He'd be up by 7am, have his breakfast, then visit his parents before starting work on the farm by 8.30am. He'd pop back to the house by 10.30am for a cup of coffee, then he'd be off again before returning for half an hour at 12.30pm for lunch. Then he'd be back at work until 5.30pm when he'd pop back to check up on his mum and dad. After a quick bite to eat, he'd be out again on the farm.

Often during the summer months he'd be up spraying crops at 3am. He was full of energy and never knew what a day's illness was like. He was strong too, although to look at him you wouldn't necessarily

15

have thought so. He'd think nothing of spending hours working on a tractor then getting out a big, heavy rotavator to turn the soil. Strawing strawberry fields is an extremely tiring job but Keith never thought anything of it.

He worked long, long hours on his own. He'd start pruning in the orchard in November and keep going right through until March, working completely alone, never once complaining. It was the same when he was working in the strawberry fields, even though there was a team of ladies who helped him there. They absolutely adored Keith. I think that's because he was a very good boss who was also prepared to lead by example by working really hard himself. At one time he even took on another area to grow apples in nearby Weeley for a while but then he stopped operating there and bought another piece of land adjacent to Greshams. This increased the acreage to 25 which, in terms of horticulture, was a pretty fair size.

As time went by we settled in nicely at Greshams and, after two years' marriage, I became pregnant with our first son Andrew. At the time I was working at a dental practice but, when I was six months' pregnant, I stopped working. When I first told Keith about the imminent arrival of a little one I was a little taken aback by his reaction. To be fair, we'd never even really talked about having a family and, in effect, Keith and I were almost in different generations. This was emphasised when I think back to when we first met. Keith was actually a friend of my parents – in fact, he was almost in the same generation as my parents. He was their friend before I ever met him. When I eventually broached the subject that I would quite like to start a family, Keith was incredulous: 'What? Oh dear, I'd never even thought about that!'

Perhaps it wasn't too surprising when I first informed Keith he was about to become a father that he didn't seem quite as excited by the fact as I'd thought he would be. I'm sure it was due to the generational thing when men didn't show their emotions as much as young men of my own generation had been brought up to do. Keith had never really been one to show his emotions and I put that down to the fact that he'd been sent away to live in a Dame's School – an old-fashioned pre-preparatory school run by two elderly ladies, in nearby Tattingstone, when he was just three and a half years old and where he remained until he was seven years old.

Keith absolutely hated it there. The experience left him with deep emotional scars and that, I'm sure, is why he was unable to express his emotions in any appreciable way until much later in life. 'Keith, I'm expecting,' I told him. 'Oh, are you? That's good,' he replied quietly. I was rather disappointed. I'd hoped he'd be jumping up and down shouting out 'Great!', but it just didn't happen like that. That said, there was no doubting Keith's excitement when Andrew was born on 21 November, 1972, and he proved to be a super dad.

I stayed in hospital for a week before returning home to Greshams and it's just as well that Andrew was such an easy baby to deal with. In those days – and particularly bearing in mind the generational thing – fathers would leave most of the responsibilities of dealing with the newborn to their mothers, and Keith was no exception – mostly, though, due to the fact that a busy farm doesn't run itself. I got a lot of help though from Keith's father who was brilliant with young children. Keith did have the paternal instinct, it's just that it took a little while for it to come to the fore.

For my part, I was pretty stubborn. I wanted to assure people that I was quite able to cope with my new baby by myself but, one day, I was absolutely shattered and, although I can remember sitting on the floor with Andrew lying on his changing mat, I can't remember anything else because I dropped off to sleep. By the time I'd woken up Keith had burped Andrew, washed him down and changed him before getting him off to sleep and laying him in his cot. He then tapped me on the shoulder and told me it was time I went to bed.

Yes, Keith was quite capable of looking after a baby, it's just that, in those days, the roles of the father and mother were far more specific than they are today, which is another reason I was not really expected to work after Andrew was born. New mums in those days were usually expected to stay at home and look after their babies. Nevertheless, I still tried to make myself useful on the farm, even if it meant I was only doing the accounts.

When Andrew was about six months old, Keith's mother became ill. She was taken in to hospital where it was expected she would have a kidney removed but it turned out she had cancer. It was a real shock to us all and we all thought we were going to lose her. She had been convinced she would never be a grandmother, particularly as Keith was well into his thirties by the time he met me. Because of the nature of her illness, we decided we would like to extend our family more quickly and, as a result, on 22 April 1974, our second son Simon was born.

Afterwards, I really didn't work much on the farm at all. Keith was really good, working hard all day on the farm to make sure it would support us all. That was always one of his main worries – that the income from the farm would be sufficient for his family. Nevertheless, we always seemed to find enough money to go on holiday and we have many happy memories of the times we went away with the boys. By now we had lots of friends to meet up with and these were such lovely times we were able to share and to look back on.

Greshams was, in fact, an idyllic place to bring up children. Yes, we had a good life and we were both very, very happy with our little family.

# DIRE STRAIGHTS

Years later I remember being told at a Parkinson's Disease meeting that the condition could be caused by a trigger point in the sufferer's life. Well, over the years, there have been several points in Keith's life that could well be responsible for the condition that struck him. Now, looking back, I can't help feeling partly responsible for Keith's health problems. Had I not been so wrapped up in my own career, had I spent more time at home, maybe Keith could have been spared some of the challenges in life he eventually had to face each day, typically without complaint.

It was after Simon was born that I became a committed Christian. Although Keith's mother survived her cancer, my father died very suddenly and unexpectedly after suffering a heart attack. Simon was only a month old at the time. As a result, my mother and my younger brother Gary came to stay with Keith and me quite often. I suppose after a family tragedy you tend to ask the big questions. What's life all about? When my mother had called me to say my father was lying on the floor, I'd hurried round, but it was too late, he had already died. I remember thinking 'is that it?'

By now my sister Catherine had become a Christian and it was she who encouraged me to find out more about the faith. I had been brought up in a Christian family but I had turned away from it. Eventually though I returned to the faith after some crunch points in my life which obviously included the death of my father. I guess his death made me think more about such matters and I became a committed Christian. I began training to become a lay reader in 1974. This must have been a very 'interesting' time for Keith because it was like I was falling in love with another man – Jesus. Suddenly, Keith had to cope with me taking on a whole new way of life, and I'm sure that must have been quite a challenge for him, particularly as the Christian way was not in his own background at all.

Meanwhile, we were kept busy working and raising our children. I was still a very bad farmer's wife – I used to pick all the wrong apples! In my defence, I was good at grading the apples, making sure that they were put onto rollers having been sorted according to their size, shape and colour before they were packed into boxes. Over the years, I took on various other jobs alongside the farm work. Keith, for his part, was working so hard, regularly getting up at 3am so he could make an early start by spraying the strawberries which, looking back, although we had absolutely no proof, Keith and I strongly suspected had made an enormous contribution to his health problems.

On **7** November 1978, our third son Ben was born. By now Keith was 44. To say Ben was a surprise would be an understatement! I had wanted another child but Keith thought he was too old to go through all that all over again. Simon had just begun school and I'd decided that Keith was probably right. As I was in training to become a lay reader I'd just accepted the fact that our family was as big as it had needed to be.

Ben's birth rather put the kybosh on all that. Nevertheless, Ben was a blessed surprise. At first Keith and I wouldn't talk about the pregnancy and, even when I was going into the maternity hospital, we had no idea what name we would be choosing for our third child. But, when Ben was born, he was absolutely gorgeous – really lovely – and we very quickly bonded together.

I think I must have been one of the first individuals they couldn't make a Reader because I was in hospital instead of Chelmsford Cathedral, trying not to have my baby five weeks early. I actually became a Lay Reader at the end of 1978.

For the uninitiated, a Lay Reader in the Church of England is a layperson who is authorised by a bishop to teach, preach and lead worship.

I was helped a lot by the parish priest of Tendring, Beaumont and Little Bentley, Frank Millar, who became a good friend who greatly encouraged me with my ministry. Frank really treated me as he would a curate rather than just a Reader which made me realise there were a lot of things I wanted to do that I couldn't do as a Reader. I wanted to be able to celebrate communion – and to conduct marriages. I wanted to preach Christ but I knew there would be plenty of obstacles along the way, plenty of doors that could be shut in my face.

Having eventually become a Reader, which I did for several years, I realised the extra pressure it was putting on Keith. Still incredibly busy holding the fort, Keith worked on, never once complaining as I followed the path of my choice. There were only two women Readers in the whole area when I was made one – but I'd never even given a thought about whether or not it was a male or female job. I just knew that it was something God was calling me to do. I knew there were no women priests but, initially, that was not even an ambition of mine as it had never entered my head that it would be a possibility, I just wanted to become a Lay Reader.

I returned to nursing in a hospital in nearby Tendring about a year after Ben was born. My return was prompted by the fact that the income from the farm, despite all Keith's hard work and long hours, was suffering dramatically. I hated working at Tendring – I remained there for a year – but, in truth, we were desperate for money to make ends meet. It seems silly that something like the building of a new road could have drastically changed our lives for the worse.

Basically, Greshams was bypassed. This had a devastating effect on the strawberries side of our business. We used to have a Pick Your Own policy and passing motorists would see the signs and, as the sign suggested, they would stop to pick their own strawberries. Now we had lost our passing trade and, to make matters worse, at least as far as Keith and I were concerned, Britain joined the European Community. Subsidies meant the prices of apples and strawberries suddenly dropped to such an extent that we were struggling to survive financially. Going back to nursing suddenly became my only choice. It was either that or go under.

Ben was cared for by my mother while I was working nights in the hospital. Andrew and Simon were at school. Because I hadn't actually finished my nursing training I was employed as an auxiliary nurse. Obviously, with Keith working all day, and me working all night, we didn't actually see a lot of each other and life soon proved a real struggle. We were so grateful for all the support we received from the family at this time.

Thankfully, the boys were not too aware of the problems Keith and I were facing. In fact, nowadays, the boys look back on their childhood days at Greshams with great affection. They particularly remember helping Keith out in the grading sheds with the apples and strawberries. Sometimes they would help out with the picking too. Simon remembers helping Keith clear a whole field with a tractor. Sam, our golden Labrador would be with them – he was also a big part of our lives. In the summer the boys thought it was great when people came to the farm to pick their own strawberries, and the boys would have great fun having raspberry fights!

Andrew recalls Greshams as being 'a dream – the perfect place for three boys to grow up in – we had so much space and freedom. We felt so secure as Dad was totally focused on the farm, he worked like a Trojan', while Simon reflects: 'Dad's work was a labour of love. He loved growing apples and strawberries. It was his passion. He just loved nature – he really must have done because now we know, there were times when he wasn't making a lot of money out of it. We had an idyllic life – I couldn't imagine growing up anywhere where we could have been happier.'

With three young children, a home and farm to run, this proved to be a most stressful and worrying period for Keith and me. From that point on, I was the main wage earner, which was really hard for Keith to accept because, until these recently arisen problems, the farm had always been able to provide us with a good standard of living.

By now Keith was 45 and reaching a time of life that many men find to be a 'crisis' period in their lives. I remember him desperately trying to come up with ideas to ease our financial burdens. He even thought about opening up a garden centre, but I wasn't keen on the idea and talked him out of it. Then he thought about the possibility of becoming a horticultural lecturer, for which he was sufficiently qualified but nothing ever came of it. Despite numerous ideas, the reality, he decided, would be to work his way through the problems by carrying on working the land at Greshams.

All through this difficult period of time I still had yearnings to follow Christ. Anyone wanting to take up the priesthood is advised to go away to a retreat, a quiet place where they can gather their thoughts for a couple of days while they decide if it is really a path they want to go down. It was while I was at the little chapel at Bradwell-on-Sea in 1981 that I became convinced that God was calling me to become a deaconess – women could not become a deacon or a priest at that time. I quite clearly heard a voice behind me saying, 'No, not yet, the doors are closed'. I looked behind me but no-one was there. I thought, 'that's odd', but the voice was right. For two more years the doors really were closed.

Was it frustrating? Well, yes and no. I'd been kept busy working as a Lay Reader and it was not until two years later that I returned to the little chapel which, this time, was crowded with people attending a pilgrimage. I found myself sitting in the same seat as before and, just as clearly, I heard a voice telling me to go forward, the doors had opened for me. I know a lot of people must feel I was going nuts hearing voices but to me it was so real, so clear that it was utterly convincing.

Then began a long drawn out process. I had to see a vocations adviser and a clergy adviser who both asked me so many probing questions . . . why do I want to do this?, what would I want to do as a minister? How would I feel if I couldn't get in? How does your husband feel about your plans? How do your children and your friends feel about it? How do you understand God and where is Jesus for you? It went on and on non-stop. Afterwards, I had to go before the director of ordinands and eventually it had to be decided whether or not to put me forward to go for an Advisory Council for Church Ministry course for which I would have to go away for three or four days with other people who were asking the same question – is ordination right for me?

Eventually I was selected and was faced with clergy and lay people who were testing me all the time as they tried to assess if my call was God's call and whether or not I wanted it for the right reasons. I came away thinking I would be happy to go with whatever decision they came to. I really felt it had been a good experience. I'd also had a lot of support from my mother as I faced entering what was, and still is, a male-dominated world. For three years I was an external student at Oakhill College in London where I travelled every

Tuesday, once a month residentially for a week and residentially for a full week each year.

The topic of women in the priesthood was a rather hot potato – there were several arguments about it but I personally never once had any opposition to my theological ambitions. In fact, in my last year of training, in 1986, I joined the Rev Peter Ball at St Mary the Virgin Church in the small Essex village of Lawford for a placement. He was so good to me, offering support and not allowing any barriers to be put before me.

By 1987 our farm was in dire straights financially. Things, after a brief rally, had gone from bad to worse. Simon and Andrew had gone off to boarding schools on assisted places and, although he was only seven years old at the time, Ben decided he wanted to go to boarding school too, which was arranged after he received a scholarship. This was a particularly bad year for the farm. It was the year of The Great Storm. Earlier that year our crop had been decimated by a massive hailstorm and The Great Storm was the last thing any farmer wanted. From that point on we knew we would be faced with the most trying of circumstances.

Once your crop has been ruined, there's no income. There was nothing we could do about it. No second chances, you just have to wait until your next crop bears fruit the following year. It was an absolutely disastrous year, just awful. The wet summer meant the strawberry crop had failed, we'd long since lost the passing trade, and then the hailstorm really crushed us. We had no savings to fall back on and, without the help of Keith's mother and father over the next few years we'd have been broke.

In 1988 I took up a position as an auxiliary nurse at St Helena's Hospice in nearby Colchester. This, at least, meant that I was able to share some of the burdens Keith had been experiencing. By now I had been ordained as a deacon but my responsibilities at the hospice involved the practical care of the patients. Although I was not employed as a counsellor I like to feel I was a good listener but I wasn't allowed to preach my faith there other than when patients asked me to do so. I remained at the hospice for a couple of years but still our money worries escalated.

To say I was relieved to be offered the position as a house mistress and religious education teacher at St Joseph's College, a Catholic school in Ipswich, would be an understatement. I took up my position in 1990 and it proved, financially at least, to be an absolute Godsend. On the other hand, my new role meant I would have to move away from home, from Keith and Greshams, and would need to live in at the college. Undoubtedly, that would put an enormous strain on our family and, in particular, on Keith – and on our relationship with each other. With the farm still struggling, the children away at school, this was a really testing time for Keith. At least I would see two of the boys, Simon and Ben, because they were pupils at St Jo's. Andrew was by now at Felsted School and, to make matters worse, in this, his upper sixth year, he was also experiencing a very difficult time.

It was while I worked at St Jo's that the rules were changed to allow women to become priests and I knew that if I went forward I would cause a great deal of heartache to some people, including many of my friends there who would never accept the possibility that a woman could become a priest. I think I was more frustrated than hurt at their stance because they could see that I had an ordained ministry and they could not help but recognise that but, because of the Catholic teaching that they were trying to abide by, they could not agree that it was right. To be fair, they were in a quandary. When the vote was taken by the General Synod to allow women into the priesthood in 1994 I noticed that some of my closest friends at St Jo's were rather quiet.

I lived in the school during the week, returning to Greshams and Keith only on Wednesdays. Living apart was hard, particularly on Keith. He was running the farm and looking after the home but, given that the farm was hardly making any money at all at the time, the work at St Jo's was a life saver for us. We needed to make ends meet. Moneywise, there's no way we could have got by financially without my work in Ipswich. These were very testing times for Keith and me but, all the time, his support for me never waivered. When I was first offered the position at St Jo's, even though Keith knew it would mean us spending so much time apart, he insisted I should go for it and reassured me that I would be very good at it. Keith would come to Ipswich and stay over at the college at the weekends or, sometimes, I would come back to Greshams, but I realise now just how stressful a time this had been for him.

Looking back, I always say this period was the best and the worst time of our lives because, for me faithwise, I grew so much. I learned so much from my colleagues at St Jo's. I loved teaching there, it was fantastic. I was even taking the children abroad and doing all sorts of wonderful things. I loved running Elwin House, I took to it like a duck to water but, meanwhile, poor old Keith was back at home, working himself into the ground, alone on the farm.

Living as I was in a boarding community, we ate together, socialised together, worked together, which is why, on some Sunday afternoons, whenever Keith was able to spend a while away from Greshams in order to travel to St Jo's to visit me, he would feel completely out of it because he didn't know anybody. Then things began to go wrong at St Jo's. People were being made redundant and I was fearful I could be next – and that was a situation we could ill afford.

I think we managed to keep our financial situation mostly unnoticed by the boys although Ben, our youngest, recalls how hard Keith and I were working quite clearly:

'I remember Dad was always working very hard – he did so all his life. After a day at work he'd visit my grandparents to have a chat with them, then he'd come home to have his tea and sit in front of the TV but it was pretty soon he'd be falling asleep. Quite often he would be setting off to work in the orchard at 5am. He was a very quiet, gentle, solid man. He took great pride in his family. He was affectionate to us boys, but not so much in a touchy-feely sort of way – that came more into play as his illness progressed much later in life.

'After he retired he was far more likely to give any one of us a hug or a kiss and to tell us how much he loved us. But, when we were children, I can't really remember Dad being greatly expressive. I can't remember a single occasion he told me or my brothers off for any reason – that was more Mum's role! That said, we would always know if he was cross because he would become very quiet, he wouldn't really want to talk about what had upset him.

'Mum reckons that when my brothers were small, Dad would play with them whenever he could particularly because he'd been working such long hours and he was just getting used to his role as a father. But, because I was born so much later on he would play with me quite a bit – probably because he'd become far more used to the idea once I'd arrived on the scene. I can very rarely recall him being upset with us – sometimes perhaps with my brothers but not with me – I was a good boy! Dad raising his voice at us or even smacking us would have been out of the question.

'I can't recall many times Dad and I went out together, although, when I was at boarding school he did come to pick me up and take me to my confirmation classes because Mum was occupied working as a nurse at the time. I remember he'd always bring me chocolate and we'd have a nice chat, just the two of us together, mostly at a child's level of conversation.

'Because of his huge workload, Dad didn't have the time to take us fishing or do things like that but he did do things for us to make up for this. I remember he made a den for us to play in in one of the fields by the farm. I remember a time when I'd kept a weather diary. Dad prepared a rain gauge for me and showed me how it worked. Little things like that were Dad's way of showing affection. Being so young I was never aware of the precarious financial situation facing Mum and Dad although this was the reason we didn't have too much quality time together.

'That said, it was my choice to go to boarding school when I was seven years old. I wanted to do the same as my older brothers. Now I realise just how hard it must have been for my parents to afford me the chance to gain a better education to benefit me later in life. They both must have worked incredibly hard to send me to Orwell Park at Nacton, near Ipswich.

'I entered there on a scolarship – but it was by no means a full scholarship. Mum and Dad had to make a significant contribution too. However, the last two years at Orwell Park were not financially viable so I left and went to St Jo's. Even with his back to the wall

27

financially and working really long hours, Dad still found the time to come to St Jo's to visit me every week.'

After being invited to take up a post as chaplain teaching RE at Benenden, a girls' public school in Kent, I left St Jo's in September 1995. This was even further away from home and, looking back, this is when, I feel, Keith was probably at his most stressed. I think Keith was changing at this time and that it was during my time at Benenden that this awful disease first struck him. Keith had never been the best of communicators but, at this time, he rarely telephoned me and, even when he did, he just seemed so odd. He just wasn't Keith. Benenden, an establishment once attended by HRH Princess Anne, was a real hot-house, you couldn't afford to give anything less than 100 per cent, but I still managed to get home once a week. I'd finish work on a Thursday evening and would travel back to Essex before returning to Kent on a Friday night.

In spite of all the stresses Keith was experiencing, it seems the arrival of Ben back at Greshams alleviated the situation to some degree. When Ben was in the sixth form he left St Jo's where he'd been boarding to became a pupil at Colchester Grammar School. That meant moving back in with his father at Greshams. That was an interesting period because, at last, he was spending a lot more time on his own with Keith and the pair of them got to know each other in a far more adult way than ever before. They would find themselves spending the evenings together. They would make a point of spending some quality time together, either watching TV or just talking. This was definitely a turning point in their relationship as it was the time Ben got to know his dad much better. Ben felt Keith would talk to him more as if he was an adult than as a child.

'This is a time in my life that I hold quite dear,' he recalls. 'Dad didn't really talk about his feelings, but more about his experiences. I remember being fascinated as he told me things about his life that I'd had no idea about. I realised Dad had a wonderful sense of humour – very dry – especially after he'd had a drink! Not that he'd ever get drunk – I never ever saw him worse the wear for drink, but a glass of something would usually be enough to loosen him up a little.

28

'Dad seemed to have the knack of knowing the exact time to drop in a couple of little words that would have everyone who heard him in fits of laughter – I guess even more so as he was so quiet it would often be so unexpected. He was always one to fade into the background – he wasn't always cracking jokes by any means but he had this wonderful impish grin which was so amusing.'

Although this was a tiring period, my spirits were uplifted when Simon announced that he and Louisa were about to become parents. That said, I thought Keith would have been quite cross at the news. Although Simon and Louisa were living together they were not married and this was at odds with Keith's morals. In fact though, he surprised me – he was really pleased. Simon and Louisa had bought a home of their own but, owing to financial difficulties, they'd no option other than give it up and to move in to the mobile home at Greshams when they ran out of money.

However, there were concerns for the baby's health during the pregnancy which proved to be traumatic for the whole family. Nevertheless, our first grandchild Jonathon was born none the worse for all the worry.

Keith was suffering from a dreadful case of influenza when Jonathon popped into the world. I'd only ever known Keith to be ill twice, once with mumps and at this time, which meant he was unable to visit our new grandson at the maternity hospital. What should have been a most joyous time in our lives soon became one of the saddest when, just a week later, Keith's father, who had been living in a mobile home in our back garden, died suddenly. He had always been a very fit and healthy man and Keith was extremely close to him. His death was an incredible shock to us all.

Meanwhile, having Simon, Louisa and new arrival Jonathon living with us put a further strain on the family finances. Ben was also back living at Greshams and travelling daily to Colchester Royal Grammar School. As a result, Keith and I found we hardly had enough money to look after ourselves, let alone four others.

With me being miles away, the burden of supporting Ben, Simon, Louisa and the baby, fell to Keith. Within the space of five months we'd had an incredibly traumatic period in our lives. After that we had Jonathon living with us for a while because Louisa was unwell and this served to add to the pressure and strains, particularly after an incident when little Jonathon nearly drowned in the bath.

The incident was nobody's fault. I remember we had a very low-level bath and, at the time, Jonathon had just learnt to walk. He dropped his feeding bottle into the bath and somehow, he managed to clamber into the bath to retrieve it. It was a very scary moment.

This happened at quite a fractious period in Simon's relationship with Louisa. It certainly wasn't an easy time. There had been several difficulties that they were trying to face up to in their lives. Eventually Louisa and Simon split up – she was having some serious health problems at the time – and she went back to live with her parents. Jonathon stayed at Greshams with Simon while she was tackling her health issues.

'My memories of Dad at this time are from a different perspective to Mum's,' says Simon. 'She remembers the pressures he was under but, looking at it another way, with her working away at Benenden, at least Dad had some of the family to keep him company on the farm. Maybe with us being around it would have helped alleviate any loneliness he may have felt while Mum wasn't there. I know he missed her a lot. Also, losing his own father had had a significant impact on Dad so maybe it wasn't such a bad thing that we were there with him.'

When, in his younger days, Keith played hockey, he would just get his head down and run with it, and that's just how he handled all these problems. Focus on the job in hand and just get on with it. In truth though, he really needed me there to share the burden but I was still the main wage earner and we simply had no other choice but for me to remain in what was a well-paid job at Benenden. Without my income I doubt if we could have survived financially.

30

# A SHOCKING DIAGNOSIS

Often, when I returned from Benenden in 1997, Keith would be suffering from the most terrible headaches. He'd never had anything like this in the past and I would spend ages gently massaging his temple to ease the pain. I could actually feel the pulse on each side of his head. I would continue the massage until I could feel the pulses become equal and the throbbing began to ease. Also at this time, Keith was diagnosed as having an irregular heartbeat, which again, was something completely new for him. Keith's heartbeat had always been so steady, solid and regular, always around 52 beats a minute, which is incredibly slow.

I was offered the opportunity to work once more at St Jo's, this time as chaplain. It was just what we needed, the opportunity to work nearer to home and to Keith. This time, however, there was a significant difference – I would not be living in – this time I'd be at home with Keith, Simon and Jonathon. Being back with Keith was a joy but suddenly I noticed just how much he had aged. Keith had never seemed to age at all but now he seemed so much older and he'd slowed right down. Work suddenly became a burden – it never had been before – as I mentioned earlier, farming was his passion. He had always told me he could never see himself ever not farming – now it was almost as if he couldn't wait to give up the farm.

I truly believe that the money worries, the death of Keith's father, the worries before and after Jonathon was born, and me being away from home so much all combined to trigger Keith's illness. Something psychologically happened to him. It became obvious to me that things were not right with Keith even before his disease was diagnosed. Things he would normally have taken in his stride he worried about. His driving became slightly erratic, and although he never recognised this, his passengers were not comfortable. Then his right leg, right arm and the right side of his body began to swell and by this I mean he *really* swelled up. It was as if he'd ballooned. It became difficult to put his shoes on and, after visits to his doctor, diagnoses of arthritis and/or gout were made. I had learned a massaging technique when working at the hospice and I used this to ease Keith's symptoms. Yet, despite suffering from considerable pain and discomfort, he continued to work non-stop on the farm.

The following year I was experiencing health problems of my own so Keith persuaded me to go to The Oaks, a private hospital in Colchester, for a check up. 'Come on,' he said, 'we'll go together.' My symptoms were as if I was having a heart attack but, thankfully, it was not as serious as that, my heart muscles were occasionally going in to spasm which is something that could be controlled by medication. That said, it was very scary whenever it happened. Maybe it was something akin to the feeling people get when they suffer from angina. Keith was very worried about me, particularly as there was a history of heart problems in my family.

At this time Keith was approaching 65 years of age so he agreed he would have a top-to-toe check up too. I went in for my check up with a BUPA Care doctor and underwent various tests and was asked to work out on a running machine. Then Keith went in for his examination and the doctor checked out his heart rate and body mass, his blood pressure and muscle tone. Then he noticed a weakness down the right hand side of Keith's body.

The doctor asked me to go back in to the surgery – not to talk about me, but about Keith. We'd both been put on a running machine and had had thorough examinations but the weakness down Keith's side had concerned him. Keith waited outside. I closed the door and sat down. 'Have you noticed anything about your husband?' the doctor asked. I told him how I thought Keith had seemed to age significantly over the past few months. 'He just doesn't move as quickly as he used to,' I said. 'Something's just not right. He's lost half a stone, his movements are awkward, he twitches all night and he's no longer interested in making love.'

'Well,' he replied, 'I think your husband may have Parkinson's Disease.' He explained that Keith's facial muscles were no longer working as they should, his responses were slow, his prostrate was enlarged and he had peticae on the skin (small reddish/purple spots caused by broken capillary blood vessels) which were a sign that platelets in Keith's blood may be abnormal. The doctor claimed he was more worried than usual. Because of the quick onset of the illness he was concerned Keith may have one of the more extreme forms of Parkinsons Disease or a Parkinson-like disease. He informed me that he had told Keith about his prostrate and blood conditions but had not shared his suspicions with him that the stiffness of Keith's limbs may indicate a form of Parkinsons Disease. A numbing fear crept over my heart. I had suspected for some time that all was not right and now I had a horrible fear that I had been right in my suspicions. I prayed that God would help Keith.

That Keith had seemed to age quite dramatically was really brought to home to me when it was time for him to meet Mr Corr, a consultant urologist. I asked Mr Corr if he would be happy if I came into the surgery with Keith. He had no problems with that at all, saying: 'Yes of course, so long as your *father* doesn't mind.' Despite the age difference between Keith and me, that was the first and only time anyone had mistaken me for Keith's daughter, such was the rate his appearance had changed.

With the prognosis about his prostrate and blood conditions in mind Keith had gone very, very quiet, as he always did when he was worried about something. He internalised his problems. I'm sure he felt his end would come very quickly – even though he was unaware at the time it was probably the basic form of Parkinson's Disease that had been predicted at that point. Keith reacted in his normal manner by keeping his thoughts to himself. He never really talked about it but I'm sure he was scared, although there's no way he would have admitted it to me at the time. He wasn't the type to make a big fuss.

As for me, well, I *was* scared. What was going on? I knew you could show Parkinson's Disease symptoms from several conditions – even from side effects of medications given for other ailments. When the possibility of a brain scan was mentioned the first thought that arrived in my head was the possibility that Keith may have a brain tumour. I guess the worst possible scenario popped into my mind. My goodness, is Keith going to die? Then my nursing experience kicked in and I told myself that this was not necessarily the case. Instead I began to hope that the scan would clear things up, that it would point us in the direction of what steps would need to be taken to sort things out once and for all.

We decided we both needed a break so we arranged to spend a few days together in Devon. It was decided that, as I had the opportunity to stay in a retreat in Kintbury in Berkshire en-route, Keith would join me there in a few days as he still had things to attend to at Greshams. Kintbury is a very, very special place for me. It's where the De la Salle brothers have a retreat. At one point the brothers ran St Jo's but that was before I ever worked there. There's an old cottage in the grounds of the retreat where I and other teachers had previously taken St Jo's pupils to give them the opportunity to experience the benefits of staying in a quiet place.

It was like going back in time whenever I went to Kintbury. When I arrived there this time I was very, very tired. It was the end of term and what with everything that had been going on at home and the stresses involved, I was more than ready to get there.

I spent the next four or five days either reading or praying. Sometimes I'd listen to music or just wind down generally. Most of the time there I was on my own so I had a lot of time to think about our situation.

I'd received Keith's medical report prior to my journey. Yes, according to the report, Keith *did* have Parkinson's Disease. That makes sense, I thought. That puts everything into perspective. As soon I was told that Keith had been displaying Parkinson's Disease *symptoms*, I'd been prepared for this verdict. I spent quite a lot of time mulling over the report and wondering how I was going to break the news to Keith when he joined me. How on earth would he react?

I spent quite a bit of time talking about our situation that week with Brother Brenet who is in charge at Kintbury. I found our conversations quite comforting but, nevertheless, when Keith was due to arrive at Kintbury, I was pretty stressed out. I was, therefore, very pleased when David, a colleague from St Jo's, who was a priest, arrived at the retreat. I remember we went for a walk and stopped at the top of a hill from which there were some amazing views. I confided in David that Keith had a 'terminal' disease. I could feel the pent-up emotions rising from within me and, although I tried so hard not to, I cried and cried and cried.

Of course, I now realise that Parkinson's Disease is not a terminal disease at all – but that's what I believed at the time. Even though I had no idea how long I was expecting Keith to live with the disease I suppose in my mind it was something that would kill him sooner rather than later. Maybe we'd be lucky if he could survive another five years? I just didn't know how I was going to be able to cope with this situation or could envisage how our lives would be changed irrevocably. It just goes to show how, when you don't know all the facts, some things can appear far bleaker than they really are. That said, at the time I had no idea that the symptoms Keith had displayed so far would be so insignificant compared to those that would follow! That was just as well as I was absolutely desolate, completely devastated. How would I see Keith through all this? Could I do it? In anybody's book, it would be quite a challenge.

Unfortunately, David knew even less about Parkinson's Disease than I did. Nevertheless, he was an absolute rock that day. 'You've got enough love to see you both through all this,' he assured me. Having him there to talk to – someone from the outside of our family circle – someone who was a very good listener was a real boon. Between them, David and Brother Brenet really helped me calm down so I could cope with Keith's imminent arrival. I can remember tossing and turning in my bed over the previous couple of nights trying to think of ways of breaking the news to Keith.

I'd forgotten a lot about Parkinson's Disease. My nursing experiences had ended a considerable time earlier and that's probably why I was allowing my mind to believe that Keith's condition was terminal. However, one thing was clear – I had to compose myself before sharing this news with Keith. I needed to be strong and calm, and I knew that now, more than ever, he would be looking to me for support. I was also aware that I would be of little use to Keith if I were to burst out in tears or showed him how scared I was for his welfare. It was time to pull myself together.

Keith had to catch a train from Colchester to Liverpool Street station in London. He then had find his way across the capital before catching another train to Kintbury. This was something most adults could do without any difficulty, Keith included – or at least that would normally have been the case. Unbeknown to me, Keith had been extremely frightened by the prospect of making this journey on his own, this being a man who, whenever we took holidays abroad, always took control of situations and could be relied upon whenever there was any interpreting to undertake. Now, however, he was frightened even when crossing the road. Had I realised just how daunting this journey was going to be for him, there's no way I would have expected him to do it alone. Bearing in mind Keith didn't actually know what was wrong with him, this must have been a particularly traumatic journey for him.

When I met him off the train though, he seemed reasonably okay. 'Hello darling, did you have a good journey?' I asked. 'Oh, so, so,' he replied, adding, 'but I wouldn't like to do it again!' The journey had really shaken his confidence. I decided I would wait until we were alone in the cottage before sharing the news with Keith. After having an evening meal at a local pub we returned to the cottage and sat down together in the lounge. Once he'd settled I decided to broach the subject.

'You remember when we took you to the hospital to have your check-up?'

'Yes'.

'How did you feel about it?'

'Okay, why?'

'Well, the doctor called me back in afterwards.'

'Did he? Why?'

'Well, he wanted to speak to me about you. You know I've been telling you that you don't move out of the way very quickly Keith, well, he thinks you may have some symptoms of Parkinson's Disease.'

'What's that?'

I tried to explain what I knew of the condition, that it affects your mobility and gives you the shakes.

'What are we going to do?' he asked.

I explained that an appointment had been made to see a consultant neurologist, Giles Elrington at The Oaks hospital in Colchester, as soon as we were home from our holiday so he could check Keith over to see what's happening. I'd like to be able to say that telling Keith had taken a weight off my mind but, in fact, it certainly hadn't. I knew this would probably be too much for Keith, in his present state, to take in and that I would probably have to shoulder the burden. It was highly likely that Keith, in the knowledge that something was wrong with him, would rely on me still further. At the time, I hadn't realised that such a reaction came with the territory – it was one of the symptoms displayed by many Parkinson's Disease sufferers.

Poor Keith, he was devastated. He didn't really *do* ill. The thought he had Parkinson's Disease put him into an instant depression. He really withdrew into himself. He didn't want to talk about it, even though *I* did. I suppose Keith just needed the time to let it sink in. Surprisingly though, we both slept quite well that night in the little cottage and, in the morning after breakfast we prepared to continue our journey down to Devon.

I can't honestly say I was in the mood for a holiday but we both certainly needed a break and it was pretty unusual for Keith to be able to get away from the farm at this time of the year – normally he'd have been dealing with his crop of apples but, this year, he'd uprooted a good number of trees – so I was determined to make the most of the time we had together while we could – after all, the future was so uncertain and I was wondering if we'd ever have the opportunity to share more holidays together. Surely Keith's diminishing health would curtail any prospect of going away together from now on.

With this in mind, we continued our journey to Devon the next day and, considering the uncertainties we were facing, we had a lovely time. We stayed in a friend's 1950s-style cottage, the weather was good and we visited lots of interesting places, although all the time I was watching Keith like a hawk, watching for symptoms or anything about him I hadn't noticed before.

We went to several National Trust houses and wandered around the gardens, we visited Clovelly where, famously, donkeys carry tourists up and down the hill. This was particularly nice for Keith because he'd been to Clovelly as a teenager. He was walking around and, to any passers-by, there was no sign that there was anything wrong with him at all. What was obvious to me though was the degree to which he had slowed down physically. Nevertheless, he seemed to enjoy the holiday, although, towards the end of each day, he was very, very tired. He rested every evening and went to bed early.

But the worries about his health were never far away from his mind. I lost count of the times he'd ask me what life would be like in the future. I explained what little I knew – that he probably wouldn't be able to do up or undo his buttons when his hands were shaking, that his co-ordination would probably decline, that he would probably require help to shave in the mornings, the latter point becoming obvious even during this holiday.

Basically, because this was an older style cottage, there was no electrical socket for Keith's shaver so he had to have a wet shave. As I watched him I noticed how slowly he did so and I ended up shaving him myself. Then I noticed how his hands seemed to be stiffening up, how he seemed to be far less dextrous than before and how, thinking-wise, he seemed to be slowing down considerably. Unusually, Keith didn't seem to want to drive at all in Devon so that task fell to me. I drove us everywhere and on the long journey home.

Two weeks later Keith and I travelled to a private hospital in Ipswich for his late afternoon appointment for a scan. It had been a long two weeks – a period when I could think of little else, and I'm sure it was the same for Keith. We just wanted answers. Fortunately, the whole process on the day was relatively straightforward. On arrival Keith had to sign in and answer several medical questions, with my help of course. He was asked what his symptoms were like at that precise moment and he had to answer lots of questions about his background and general health. Fortunately, there wasn't too much waiting around before Keith was called through to another room for his scan. I had to wait outside the door. Fully dressed, Keith had to lay very still on the scanner which, in itself, must have been a very claustrophobic experience for him. Fortunately, the whole process only took around 20 minutes, but that's plenty long enough if it's happening to you. The scanner took images in slices of Keith's brain as if they were slices of bread.

38

I suppose I'd been hoping to find out something straight after the scan but, of course, this was not the case. The radiographers are not supposed to tell you anything, the results have first to be passed on to the consultants for review before a patient is told anything. That said, Keith's radiographer did offer one comment after the scanning process. Looking at the scans he just said, 'I think they look okay,' which came as a huge relief. Any more we wanted to know would have to come from Giles.

This was of little comfort as far as Keith was concerned. Although he'd seemingly passed this examination he was by now aware that he still had major health issues. He responded by throwing himself into his work and was reluctant to talk about the subject. Prior to the scan he'd felt it was better to worry about what you can deal with rather than something you can't – that's his way – but I could tell that he was really worried.

I'm sure that as far as Keith was concerned his life was over once Parkinson's Disease was diagnosed. This was the end. Can't change it, best to just get on with things while he could. He cut himself off from his friends and was unwilling to go out socially, preferring to concentrate solely on the farm. He didn't want to talk about his illness, he lost interest in life and was unwilling to make any plans at all.

Like Keith, I also threw myself whole-heartedly into my work at St Jo's. I'd look for anything possible to do, anything that would help take my mind off what was happening to Keith. But, no matter how hard I tried, I found it so difficult to concentrate on my teaching. Always, at the back of my mind, and often to the front of it, were my concerns for my husband and the uncertainty of our future together. At least I had some terrific moral support from my colleagues at St Jo's which was greatly appreciated at a time when I needed it most.

Meanwhile, as the days passed, Keith was increasing his reliance on me. With his confidence at such a low ebb, I became his safety net. He only seemed to feel safe when I was near him. Then he suddenly decided, at the age of 65, he would now retire. This came as a huge surprise to me. A few months previously this would have been the very last thing on his mind.

I must admit to feeling pretty scared and sorry even for myself. Keith and I had just endured 10 very difficult years and now the prospect of us enjoying our twilight years happily and healthily together had been blown to smithereens. In a way I felt cheated.

The realisation that Keith's illness would affect both our lives to a very significant degree was hard to take in or accept. Keith had been looking forward to maybe joining a bowls club – something he would really have liked to do – yet suddenly he realised it was not to be. How on earth would Keith cope with this, I wondered. Keith had always been so active. How would he fill his days? He never sat still. What was life going to be like if he couldn't get out of his chair? And, quietly, I was thinking to myself: 'Will I have enough love to cope? Will I be able to see this through to the end?'

Within days of returning from Devon we arrived for Keith's appointment with consultant neurologist Giles Elrington at The Oaks hospital in Colchester. We didn't realise it at the time but we were meeting for the first time a man who would have a significant impact on the quality of both our lives in the forthcoming years – a man we would become forever indebted to.

Giles is undoubtedly in my mind a very clever man – though he modestly begs to differ! He has a particular subspeciality in both headache and multiple sclerosis and has published a good number of research articles and book chapters on the subject of migraine and neurology for healthcare professionals. He received his MB BS from St Bartholomew's Hospital in 1980 and a MRCP (UK) from the Royal College of Physicians in 1983, passing on his first attempt. Four years later he gained his FRCP title from the Royal College of Physicians and then, in 1990, qualified with an MD from the University of London.

It had been three weeks since Keith had been examined by our BUPA Care doctor and we were desperate for some form of encouragement, just a little snippet of positive information that we could cling on to.

Unbeknown to us though, Giles had something else in mind. Having compared notes with the other doctor, Giles had been concerned Keith may be suffering from a particularly ruthless form of

Parkinson's Disease and that the brain scan would provide evidence of whether or not his hunch was correct.

I've read that we're all losing dopamine, a neuro-transmitter which is released from the substantia nigra area of the brain, and that gives us the potential to suffer from Parkinson's Disease. It seems that those who actually suffer from Parkinson's Disease face a steeper dip in their dopamine levels.

When a person displays Parkinson's Disease symptoms there are a whole range of illnesses that it can be. Some of them progress very quickly, others very slowly. Because of the speed of changes in Keith's health, Giles thought he may have what he felt was one of the 'very, very, very fast forms of the disease'. If Keith had that, Giles did not expect Keith to survive much more than a year.

As soon as Keith walked into the room Giles said: 'I know exactly what's wrong with you, now tell me your symptoms.' I didn't realise at the time that Parkinson's Disease patients have a certain 'look' about them – although I can easily recognise it these days. I can easily spot someone I don't know in the street and know they are Parkinson's Disease sufferers. Sometimes I even wonder if *they* know they have Parkinson's Disease yet. It just jumps out at me.

Giles took Keith into a room so they could be alone and he conducted a series of physical tests on Keith. Afterwards, I was called in as Keith was asked to explain how he'd been feeling. Giles demonstrated a classic test of Parkinson's Disease by tapping his finger above Keith's nose between the eyebrows and Keith responded by several quick flicks of his eyelids. Normally, the eyelids would only flicker once. However, when Giles observed Keith's scan he was hugely relieved to tell us that things maybe were not quite as bad as he had anticipated. 'Thank goodness for that, I can't see what I was expecting to see on Keith's scan,' he told us. The plaques and shrinking of the brain he had anticipated were not apparent on the scans. 'That's the good news,' he said, adding: 'It looks like we're dealing with straightforward Parkinson's Disease after all, and people can live with that for 20 or more years.'

Giles explained that there are some extremely fast acting brain disorders that can cover a wide spectrum of diseases that can present with Parkinson's Disease symptoms – and then there's a very extreme one that's incredibly rapid which often limits the sufferer to one, maybe two years more life expectancy. With this, the shrinking of the brain is very apparent. Giles had been expecting to see a number of scars on Keith's brain scan which do not respond so positively to medication for Parkinson's Disease.

We asked Giles if Keith would need to give up driving. 'No, no,' he said, 'you'll know yourselves when it's time to give up.' My first questions were 'what are the consequences?', 'how quickly does this happen?', 'what do we need to do next?', 'what causes it?', 'how do we cope with this?', 'what will Keith need?' – my questions were almost endless.

During the build-up to this appointment, at the backs of our minds there had been the possibility that Keith may have Nv CJD as some of his symptoms were developing so quickly and were similar to those experienced by a very close friend of Andrew's shortly before she succumbed to the disease at the tender age of 25. Memories of her battle with Nv CJD were still very fresh in our minds so it was perhaps only natural we – and particularly Andrew – would notice the symptoms she endured. She had suffered from bad co-ordination, she'd had the shakes and the negative thoughts and depression, just as Keith had experienced.

That Giles couldn't see anything wrong with Keith's scan was very reassuring. Sadly, though, that reassurance turned out to be seriously misplaced. Little did we know at the time that the plaques really *were* there but at this time Keith was still in the very early stages of his illness so they were not visible to the naked eye. Our relief at the time, although so tangible, proved to be premature – the ruthless disease that Giles had so feared to be forming in Keith's brain would soon make its presence felt and with it, our lives would never be the same again.

# A GATHERING STORM

During my nursing training at Addenbrookes Hospital I had hated the aspects of neurological and geriatric care – little did I know then that I would be spending a large part of my life doing just that for my husband! At Addenbrookes, we had been in the very early days of using a drug known as Leva Dopa to treat Parkinson's Disease. In those days it had proved very difficult to control the dosage of this drug, because, although it had a very quick effect in stopping the shaking that presents itself with Parkinson's Disease, the benefits could also diminish very quickly, prompting the bigger shakes all over again. Other times, it may not have acted quickly enough and the patient could go into major shakes. I can still remember a lady who was absolutely rigid – she could hardly move – but, after receiving Leva Dopa, it released her and her movement became more fluid and she could walk once again.

Since those days, however, I understand the medication has been significantly refined and improved. I'd also had some experience of working with patients with Alzheimer's Disease during my time at Tendring Hospital, but I'd never had any personal experience of dealing with it.

Giles was marvellous. When Keith asked him whether or not he'd be 'losing his mind', Giles replied: 'You don't lose your marbles with Parkinsons, they just get a bit muddled up,' which, I felt, was a very gentle way of explaining it. I'd always felt able to deal with people with physical problems, but I never felt confident dealing with people with mental difficulties. Knowing what or what not to say to people unable to respond to me had always concerned me. I was worried as to how well I would be able to support Keith. However, when we came out of our meeting with Giles I was in a reasonably positive mood. 'Okay, so it's *only* Parkinson's, we can deal with that.' By this time I had searched the internet to find out as much as I could about Parkinson's Disease and I have to admit, it was quite a relief at the time to know what we were dealing with.

Once home I contacted the boys. It was time to call a family conference, a chance to tell them all we could about their father's illness and to try to answer any questions they may have. They were all shocked to hear the diagnosis but I should have realised how supportive the boys would be. I just cannot underestimate how great a part they all since played in helping me with Keith's subsequent care. Each of them instantly assured me that they would be there for me and that they would support their dad and me – 'we can do this Mum, we'll do it together' – and, to their credit, they kept to their word right to the very end.

Although terribly shocked by the news, Andrew pointed out that people can live with Parkinson's Disease, after all, former world heavyweight boxing champion Muhammad Ali has been coping with it for years. Okay, it was a long term illness but Ali was still leading a high profile, public life.

Simon didn't know much, if anything, about Parkinson's Disease at the time but he had already noticed how Keith had been walking with a limp. He was quite shocked to hear the diagnosis, even though he didn't really know what it was. Then he began to wonder how long his Dad would live. He didn't know whether or not Parkinson's was a terminal illness, but he couldn't help wondering if it could be.

Ben, in particular, found the news very tough to cope with. His girlfriend at the time, Kelly, was away. Ben had been working in London. He remembers calling her, quite upset. Otherwise he thought he was all right. 'I tend to be an optimist and was thinking 'what could we do next?' he said. 'I think it all rather hit me during the following term at university. I had a 6,000 word extended essay to write which meant I had to work very closely with my tutor. I was covering a topic each week which had to be amalgamated into a larger piece of work. I produced my essay which, looking back, I have to say was pretty average at best. My tutor wasn't impressed, gave it back to me and I made a few changes before handing it back.

'I remember her looking at me and saying 'What the hell is going on here? This is not the level of work I expect from you. I was expecting a brand new essay but you've only altered a couple of things. What are you doing here if you're not prepared to do the work?' That was it – the moment I just broke down completely. I was crying uncontrollably – I just could not stop. I remember my tutor, who was a lovely woman, asking me what had happened, what was wrong with me. To be honest, up until that point, I hadn't realised there had been anything wrong with me but I guess I'd just been bottling everything up and, suddenly, my emotions had just all come tumbling out.

'For at least five minutes I couldn't even speak. Eventually I was able to blurt out that Dad was really ill and that I didn't know how to cope with it. I have to say she was wonderful. 'Don't worry about the work for now, go away and calm down, we'll deal with this later.' And then we had a long chat.

'I remember returning to my room to find Kelly had come to see me. She asked me what was wrong and, basically, for the next hour, I just had to cry it all out. This really helped to release the pressure that, unknown to me, had been building up inside of me. I'd come to the point when it had finally hit me just what a serious thing Dad and the family were now facing. This, I realised, was something we were ALL going to have to deal with.'

Giles prescribed a drug called Sinemet and, amazingly, Keith responded to a small dose quite magnificently and there was a massive physical improvement. Giles had prescribed the right dose immediately – and we knew it didn't always work like that. Within days the change in Keith had been quite incredible.

After a further consultation Giles told us he could see what he'd been expecting to see – Keith's responses were much quicker and his movements much more fluid, and he was able to do so many things he'd been unable to do prior to taking the Sinemet. His co-ordination improved significantly, his face changed – he'd become very flat faced, just as many people with Parkinsons appear, almost expressionless, and unable to show any signs of happiness – but now he looked alert and almost back to normal. However, Keith had had no idea of the physical changes in his appearance, not at all. Nevertheless, I was absolutely delighted. Keith was still becoming a little muddled at times, but it wasn't that bad, and this was attributed to the Sinemet which also has a tendency of increasing susceptibility to hallucinations.

All this coincided with positive moves with my ministry. The opportunity came to move to full-time parochial ministry in nearby Lawford where I'd had a placement during my last year of training. A few months later, Keith wound up the business, just tilling the fields to keep them in a reasonable state as we prepared to sell the house and land at Greshams. Keith and I had decided we needed to spend a little more time together.

Keith didn't seem to be faring too badly and the fears I'd had while we were in Devon that it would most likely have been our last holiday together appeared to be unfounded. We decided to book a holiday by Lake Garda in Italy and, on the whole, we had a super time. However, I remember being conscious of the fact that Keith was slowing down quite a lot.

There's a beautiful hill overlooking Lake Garda. It was possible to walk through some beautiful gardens on the way up the hill, which we did two or three times but I was aware of it being a real effort for Keith. Normally, it would have been me struggling up the hill following as Keith bounded on ahead of me, but now we had to stop on regular occasions. We were still able to do whatever we wanted to do but I became aware of the fact that he was leaving it to me to organise everything. He wasn't getting muddled but it was just that he didn't want to be in control, to make decisions. Normally we'd have decided jointly what to do each day but now he was far happier for me to suggest whatever we should do.

Other things about his behaviour struck me. He would start worrying excessively as to whether we had enough money and he was beginning to tire much more quickly. Nevertheless, no-one else would have suspected he had Parkinson's Disease as he was still eating normally and was happy to swim each day in the lake. As long as he was taking his medication he was okay and, once home again, he was still able to drive the car and to use the ride-on mower in the garden.

In September 2000, after I'd finished my work at St Jo's and once we'd sold Greshams, we moved to the nearby village of Lawford. Because of all the upheaval and the increased workload that came along with my new ministry, things were pretty hectic for a while.

The following Easter, Keith and I took another holiday, this time in a self-contained apartment at a lovely complex known as Manoir De Hilguy in Britanny, northern France. We left in the evening on Easter Sunday. It was a much-needed break, particularly as I had still been incredibly busy with taking in everything that a new ministry involves and having moved house.

I suppose I had taken my eye off the ball to some degree as far as Keith was involved because of my hectic schedule and I must admit I was quite shocked to see the decline in his health once we arrived in France. He was confused, stumbling over his words and stammering. Inside the small apartment he'd forget where each room was.

There was a central office within the complex where they kept things like DVDs and so on and where you went if you wanted to use the swimming pool and the clubhouse. To get into the office you needed to remember a key code which Keith was unable to do and, even when I helped him, he seemed unable to understand how to use the touch-button pad. Normally I might have asked him to pop over to the office to get a DVD for us to watch in the evening, but this was completely beyond him now – he couldn't even find the clubhouse, even though it was so close to our flat.

As a result, he couldn't be left alone, not even for a moment. After hardly being at home to being with Keith 24 hours a day, I was terribly shocked at the degree to which he had deteriorated. He was extremely restless at night, suddenly jerking in a way people do when they try to stay awake when they're almost asleep. Keith was like that all night long and we were hardly getting any rest at all. We endured some very disturbed nights with lots of twitching going on and some really distressing nightmares. In the daytime he would simply 'lose' himself, writing in the air with his hands which is normally a symptom associated with very ill people who are on morphine towards the end of their lives – and that frightened me very much, having seen it so often when I worked in the hospice. It seems their imaginations are taking them somewhere else.

We'd enjoy our breakfasts outside on the balcony each morning but, by the afternoons, Keith would become extremely tired and would just sleep and sleep, even though the weather outside was absolutely beautiful. There were some lovely facilities at the complex where holidaymakers could either swim, play croquet or tennis but Keith was not even slightly interested in joining in with any of them which was so unlike him.

Back home, Keith had still been driving but, here in France, there was no way he would attempt to drive. He just refused point blank to drive, even when I suggested that by doing so he'd be giving me a break. He wouldn't say 'I can't,' he'd simply say he wouldn't do it. I suggested that, instead, he should navigate. Keith was always very good at map reading but, during this holiday, it seemed that every time we ventured out in the car, our apartment had moved somewhere else before we returned! He seemed to have lost the ability to fathom out how to follow a map and totally lost his sense of direction.

At this time I was in agony, having somehow strained my neck. I really would have appreciated someone else taking on a share of the driving. Eventually I had to find an osteopath to manipulate my neck for me, such was my discomfort. Normally, under these circumstances, Keith would have been the first to look up a suitable medic and to make all the arrangements for me to obtain an appointment. He would have picked up the telephone and spoken to someone in French.

My skills at speaking French are rather limited, but Keith could speak the language well. He would have taken good care of me. Now he couldn't and it was left to me to get someone to understand what my problem was and to organise an appointment to get it sorted. All of a sudden, I noticed how Keith's speech had changed. He was stumbling over his words, almost stammering and stuttering. Don't get me wrong, what he was saying was making sense, it's just that the sentence would come out very muddled.

'What would you like for tea tonight, Keith?'

'F-f-f-f-f . . . . fish'.

Otherwise he'd say the wrong word completely. I was really worried, this was not like Keith at all. Sometimes, what he was saying was just not relevant to the occasion. It was as if his mind had suddenly jumped forward or back.

Holidays had always been so important to both of us – we'd both always really looked forward to them and enjoyed them, but this one was becoming quite an ordeal as Keith's condition was rapidly deteriorating before my eyes. Having said that, we still managed to have a few good times, visiting French markets – which Keith loved as he wandered around all the stalls – enjoying coffees in the sun or driving along the coast roads, sometimes parking up somewhere and taking in the spectacular views across the sea.

Britanny is blessed with some magnificent scenery and we particularly enjoyed stopping the car to take in the views of the Atlantic coast. However, once I'd parked the car at what I considered to be a particularly stunning viewpoint and was ready to get out to go for a walk, Keith declined, preferring to stay in the car instead. Normally Keith loved walking – he would have been striding off along the clifftops with me struggling to keep up with him. It was as if he was now almost frightened to leave the car, very frightened that he might get lost. His disorientation had left him feeling particularly vulnerable and, consequently, he wouldn't let me out of his sight.

I too was feeling pretty vulnerable at this time. Here I was, in a foreign country where I had only a limited understanding of the language. I was feeling responsible for both of us and, for the first time, truly understanding that there was something else going on inside Keith's brain that would undoubtedly affect both our lives in the future.

Back in our apartment, Keith suddenly began 'seeing things'. He was noticing shapes, animals or spiders on the floor. Nothing I could say would convince him that, in reality, there was nothing there at all. It wasn't as if Keith was frightened by what he was 'seeing', he'd just spend ages staring at something that wasn't there. The first time it happened, I asked Keith what he was staring at. 'It's a spider.' 'What! Where is it?' I cried out – I'm a real coward, totally frightened by spiders. 'Has it moved?'

'No, it's right there,' Keith replied as he pointed to a blank spot on the floor. Then he 'saw' a dog, and later he 'saw' another one. From the early days of Keith's illness I had noticed how his spatial awareness was not as it should be. Simple things like not moving out of the way, not realising that he was standing far too close to me in the kitchen while I was holding hot pans were worrying developments. This was improved to some degree when Keith was taking the Sinemet, but what was happening here in France was more mental than physical – you could just see the confusion in him.

Our time in France emphasised to me the complete changes in Keith's mental and physical well-being. At the beginning of our holiday I must admit to having been rather frustrated at Keith's 'unwillingness' to get involved in anything. We were on holiday after all – here was a chance to relax and have a bit of fun at the same time, especially with such lovely facilities on hand. However, within a short time the penny dropped when it became obvious to me that Keith wasn't being awkward in any way, something was wrong.

I realised that Keith's deterioration had probably developed while we were back at home but I guess I'd been so busy, so wrapped up in my own world, that I just hadn't noticed what was going on, and that made me feel more than a little guilty. We came home via Plymouth quite late at night. We needed to find a particular place to stay before continuing our journey back to Essex the following day but Keith couldn't even read the road signs for me. We eventually found our accommodation at around 2am because I kept getting lost as I tried to drive and read a map at the same time. Normally Keith would have had no problem map reading at all. Suddenly he was jumpy again and he seemed to be going downhill fast.

The first time we met Giles he had explained that it wouldn't be necessary for us to see him again unless we felt we really needed to. If Keith's medication needed adjusting we could just visit our local GP. However, in the wake of Keith's symptoms in Britanny, I'd become very concerned for his welfare. I didn't even bother contacting our GP and got in touch with Giles directly. 'I'm sorry Giles, we've just got to see you, things have changed.'

When we arrived at Giles' office I explained what had happened while we'd been on holiday and I told him how concerned I'd been. As soon as Keith walked into Giles' room Giles could see straight away the change in him. I explained that, at times, things had seemed really bad – while at other times it was as if there was nothing wrong with Keith at all – he would appear absolutely lucid and 'with it'. He'd change from one state to the other in a flash.

At times I'd be left wondering if I'd just imagined the way Keith had been just a moment earlier. I could ask Keith what day of the week it was and ask him to write something down and he'd do it in an instant, without the slightest problem but a moment later he wouldn't be able to do either.

Giles conducted a series of mental tests on Keith. He asked him to count backwards from 100. No problem, Keith did it perfectly. I felt such a twit. Would Giles think I was I making a mountain out of a molehill? Further questions such as how old are you, when were you born, who is your wife, were all answered correctly without hesitation, yet days earlier, while we'd been on holiday, Keith couldn't even remember where we lived.

'What day is it? What date is it? and so on. Keith was fine, he could do any of the tests Giles put before him. 'Can he always do this?' asked Giles. 'No,' I replied.

I told Giles about the conversations Keith had been having with people who were not really there. Keith too was able to clearly describe the sort of things that had been happening to him, things that had really been worrying him.

'Does Keith see things?' Giles asked me. 'Does he have hallucinations?'

'Yes,' I replied.

'Does he still dress himself?'

'Yes.'

'Can he go to the loo by himself?'

'Yes.'

. . . and then Giles added: 'Has he tried to kill you yet?'

'No,' I quickly replied defensively although in fact, *he had* . . . he'd had a nightmare and thought I was a rope and he'd started to strangle me.

I realised Giles was trying to paint a picture in my mind of what the future may hold.

'You must think I'm going mad Giles,' I said almost apologetically.

'Not at all,' he replied, 'I know exactly what's happening, Keith is

51

displaying the symptoms of a condition known as Diffuse Lewy Body Disease.'

Neither Keith or I had ever heard of it.

'What on earth is that?'

Giles explained that Lewy Body was one of the most common forms of dementia, Alzheimer's Disease being the most common. DEMENTIA . . . that was the first time the word had been uttered as far as Keith was concerned. 'Oh my goodness,' I thought, 'this is a whole new ball game altogether.' This was something *really* scary. Needless to say I was in total shock when Giles gave us his prognosis. I was horrified, stunned. What can you say when you hear such a thing?

As for Keith, I'm not sure how much of it he could really take in, particularly as he'd been more than a little confused recently – even a simple task such as signing his name could be problematic for him. When the penny dropped Keith was absolutely horrified. His aunt, at about this time, was in the final stages of Alzheimer's and Keith had been listening to his cousins talking about her condition. This added to his fears even more. Keith never said a word. He just did what he always did in a crisis – he disappeared into his shell. It was left to me to ask all the questions while Keith sat there speechless, in total shock.

Giles then moved swiftly on to the more practical nature of our dilemma: 'Does your bank account have joint names?' I told Giles that most of our accounts were in joint names, though Keith did possess one account in his name only. 'You need to get that account into joint names,' advised Giles, 'and I think you need to do that now rather than in a month or six weeks' time,' – that's how fast he reckoned things could move on. In six weeks' time, Keith would probably be incapable of doing any form of paperwork. What a dreadful thought.

After the meeting with Giles, Keith and I did the sensible, practical thing. We headed directly into Colchester town centre, had a cup of tea at a department store then went straight to the NatWest bank to convert Keith's account into a joint one. We then made an appointment to see our solicitor to organise me having power of attorney over his affairs.

As Giles had said, things with Keith had been deteriorating fast, and time was of the essence. We were at a stage when Keith really needed to do things at his own pace, his mind could hardly cope with sudden changes, but we needed to act at once even though it was important to keep him calm. Then a worrying thought suddenly hit me. What if something happens to me? Who would look after Keith? It's all very well me having power of attorney over his affairs, but who will care for Keith if I go before him?

Most of the journey home was in silence. Understandably Keith was terrified of what may be happening to him in the future and I was still in shock. However, after a while I tried to repeat as much as I could remember of what Giles had explained to us because I knew Keith hadn't been able to absorb it in the first instance. I knew too that Keith was doing just the same as I was, silently thinking about the future and what it would have in store. I wasn't tearful, at least, not that day – maybe it had been a good thing to leave Giles and to go straight out to do something practical, something useful – but there would be plenty of time for the tears to flow later.

We had to telephone the boys to let them know about the new diagnosis. As always, I made a point of letting them know the situation straight away. Another family conference followed but, owing to the huge shock we'd had, I was finding it difficult to answer all the boys' questions.

Like me, Ben hadn't heard of the disease before. He'd thought all along that Keith had Parkinson's Disease and he had prepared himself for the effects of that. Ben's main concern related to how the diagnosis would affect his father's mind. He tried to imagine how he'd have felt if he'd been diagnosed with the same disease. He comforted himself that, if the disease would progress as rapidly as I'd been told it would, Keith would probably suffer less than those of us around him.

As Ben said later: 'What was happening to Dad was clearly not following any course you could predict. I had the feeling we should take each week or month as it comes. I guess I had an outside view because I wasn't living at home at the time. It's like when you see someone's young child every two or three months, you notice the difference in them more than you would if you saw them each day.

'That was the kind of perspective I was getting whenever I came home to see Mum and Dad. I could often see a marked change in him – even though Mum had prepared him for my visit by saying something like 'Ben's coming to see you soon' so he might remember who I was. Poor Mum was seeing Dad's condition changing up and down every single day and her mood would go up and down with it. Some days she'd seem very positive, other days just the opposite.'

It was decided we would make another appointment with Giles to discuss the prognosis further. I telephoned Giles and asked him if I could speak with him again in order to glean more information about Keith's prospects and how best to help him. Giles agreed that, subject to us having Keith's permission to do so, he would be willing to talk to Andrew and I without the need for Keith to be present. At first Keith was rather wary of this. Would Giles be telling Andrew and I things he hadn't felt able to discuss in front of him? I explained to Keith how I needed to get everything straight in my mind if I was going to be able to help him. I promised Keith I would tell him everything Giles told us when we got back home. Keith agreed and an appointment was arranged.

I have to say, Giles was just brilliant. He didn't pull any punches at all and was so patient as he answered our questions and went through everything he thought we needed to know.

'If this is what it is, it'll be a rapidly moving illness.'
'How rapid, one year, two years?' I asked.
'How old is Keith?'
'He's 67.'
'Well, he might make 70, but it'll probably be best if he doesn't.'

Having Keith's prognosis spelled out in such a stark way was absolutely devastating. You are looking at the person you know and love and you realise there's no going back – ever. There's no second chance. This is it. This is normality now.

'Will Keith know who we are?'

'He might know who you are but he probably won't know you're his wife. He'll probably recognise you as someone he knows but he won't know how he knows you. He won't necessarily recognise your voice or be able to communicate with you and it won't be long until he'll find he can't walk.'

Giles suggested it may even be necessary to consider selecting a nursing home to care for Keith in the future. It was heartbreaking stuff. Once home, all the boys, Keith and I had a long talk and decided this was a battle we would all need to fight together. Keith had always been there to support us – now it was our turn to support him.

Andrew recalls his shock and devastation at the news. 'I had heard the doctor's explanation and how short Dad's life expectancy was. I was upset to learn of the potentially horrific pace of the disease and the resultant mental and physical degradation. I just hoped my Dad would be able to die with some sort of dignity.'

Simon, however, looked at the news from a slightly different perspective: 'Diffuse Lewy Body Disease? – I'd never even heard of it. Again, it was a shock to hear the news. The first time around we'd been told it was Parkinson's Disease, now it was something else. But, in some respects, it was quite a relief because we now had an accurate diagnosis as to what was wrong with Dad. That, surely had to be a good thing? I guess I tried to remain quite positive. At least now we knew what we would be fighting.'

# A MIRACLE – AND SCARY CUSHIONS!

Diffuse Lewy Body Disease . . . what a strange name. Suddenly a disease we had never even heard of was dominating all our thoughts. I acquired an insatiable thirst for knowledge about the condition and opted to search the internet to find out more. Much of what I found was absolutely terrifying, mostly describing how fast the disease would progress. Looking back, I certainly wouldn't recommend anyone trying to find out specific details online. Some sites were more positive than others, some were helpful and some confusing.

I went back to see Giles to obtain more information from him and I read just about everything I could find on the subject. I suppose I felt so alone because I didn't know of anyone else who was caring for someone who had this. It was easy to think Keith was suffering from an unusual disease, but then, I discovered, it's not, it's one of the most common forms of dementia. That's when I finally realised there must be many people out there with this condition who have very little idea of what it is.

I learned that Lewy bodies were named after Dr Friedrich Lewy who first discovered them at the turn of the 20th Century. They are protein deposits in nerve cells of the substantia nigra section of the brain (which is one of the regions responsible for movement control) and the cerebral cortex (the primary thinking area of the brain). The Lewy bodies, basically, interrupt messages sent out by the brain. They are also apparent in the brains of sufferers of Parkinson's Disease.

Diffuse Lewy Body Disease is often referred to as either DLB, Lewy Body Dementia, Cortical Lewy Body Disease, Lewy Body variant of Alzheimer's Disease, or Senile Dementia of Lewy Body Type.

Although the disease is often difficult to diagnose, restlessness, disturbed sleeping patterns, confusion, nightmares, visual hallucinations, 'funny turns', fainting and a fluctuation of abilities on a sometimes hourly basis are among the symptoms. I learned that there is a 2:1 male to female ratio in the disease, and that most sufferers are in their late sixties. Spatial disorientation, memory loss, slowness, muscle stiffness, trembling and shuffling are often apparent with sufferers. Symptoms will vary from patient to patient. It is a degenerative disease that, over time, causes a patient to become demented. There is no cure.

Therapy is limited to managing any neuro-psychiatric disturbances and associated movement disorders. It is believed that sufferers require similar treatment to those with Alzheimer's Disease – in fact there is some debate as to whether or not they are truly different diseases or just different symptoms on opposite ends of the spectrum of the same disease. However, the Alzheimer's Society's own website stresses the importance of an accurate diagnosis as people with Diffuse Lewy Body Disease have been known to react very badly to certain forms of medication.

There is no definitive method of diagnosing Diffuse Lewy Body Disease – at least not while the patient is alive. To date, no blood tests, CAT or MRI scans, spinal fluid or neurological tests have been conclusive, nor has anyone yet determined the probable cause of the disease.

Everything I learned seemed negative. It certainly made pretty depressing reading. I realised we were in for a tough time – and that we would require a good amount of assistance to see ourselves through it. Looking back, over several months, we had been receiving informal help and support from family members and parishioners which was very much appreciated. Marshall Guarnieri, who tended the churchyard at the time, would often sit with Keith for a couple of hours if I needed to pop out for a while. At that point, that was fine. Marshall would come in and make himself and Keith a cup of coffee and just make sure that Keith was all right.

Sylvie Howes, who would come in to help clean The Rectory, would also help to keep an eye on Keith from time to time but, one day, when I came home she'd told me 'I don't think I can continue to do this, Pat. Keith keeps taking his trousers off!' Heaven knows why. Maybe he thought it had been time to go to bed. Mary Nunn and Barbara Potter were two friends who often offered to sit with Keith. Another friend, Len Sage, was fantastic. He lives in the village and he would sometimes take Keith with him to play bowls or for a ride in the car, or out to tea.

With this support, I'd decided I would be able to help Keith by myself. I knew the boys would be able to offer extra back-up when I needed it, and Keith was still able to do some things, although this would progressively become less and less and less over a short period of time. Of course, this also meant he could rarely be left alone, which made life particularly difficult when you realise that life as a village rector can sometimes be quite chaotic.

However much you try to organise your working day and your life, there's always something unexpected cropping up to disrupt your plans. Funerals are an obvious example. I was in a career where I had to be able to adapt to situations as they happened which, obviously, made it difficult when trying to organise a structured schedule at home for Keith.

Looking after Keith and holding down a full-time job in the parish proved to be very, very tiring. By this time I was quite exhausted. Long periods of being unable to rest were really starting to take their toll. Meanwhile, unbeknown to me, the boys were becoming frustrated that I was spending so much time at work. It was after a New Year's meal that things finally came to a head.

Ben recalls: 'This is as much a story about Mum as it is about Dad. Looking back I don't think my brothers and I fully recognised the pressure Mum was under. Dad had just started to show signs that he needed care – proper care. This coincided with the time that Mum was at the peak of her involvement with the church – and her work was taking up an awful lot of her time. She was working incredibly hard.

'My brothers and I were sitting down at the dining table after a New Year's meal and it became apparent that we were almost accusing Mum of making the wrong decisions about the amount of time she was spending looking after Dad. We hadn't taken into account the fact that she needed the outlet of her work for her creative and spiritual well-being in her own life as it had been her dream to become a parish priest. I guess we were on our high horses as we began to tell her 'this is what Dad needs' although in a more subtle way than it sounds.

'Poor Mum, she just broke down in tears. 'You're accusing me, aren't you,' she said, 'but I can't just give up what I do – I can't just give up everything to look after Dad'. Seeing Mum so distressed was what it took to make the three of us fully realise that Mum needed more of our support. She needed us to share the burden of looking after him.

'As a result, we literally went away and drew up a timetable to be there more often to help out. It just wasn't fair that we'd left Mum to bear such a heavy burden on her own. For me, this was a real breakthrough moment, the realisation that, if you're a carer, you're more than just a carer.

'For us to almost demand that Mum gave up her life to care for Dad while we just carried on with ours was entirely unfair. Maybe we'd been building up a lot of anger – probably against the disease itself – but we had been projecting that anger towards Mum.

'It took her breaking down to show us just how difficult she'd been finding it to cope with the situation. This belated realisation was, I'm sure, the moment we all became aware that looking after Dad would, in future, need to be a real team effort for everyone in the family, not just Mum.'

Andrew's memories of that evening are more hazy than Ben's but, nevertheless, he agrees that I needed to put time aside for my own sanity. 'Dad was by now getting far worse health-wise,' he recalled. 'At the same time, Mum's commitments at the church were considerable, but that was also her way of coping with the situation at home. It wasn't a form of escapism, but it did give her the opportunity to talk to people outside of the home environment and that was something she badly needed, particularly as a normal conversation with Dad was no longer possible.

'For my part, I was particularly concerned Mum would burn herself out. I've since grown to fully appreciate just how important it is for people who act as carers to have someone else to look out for them. The physical and mental demands on a carer are massive so anyone finding themselves in such a position really shouldn't be afraid to ask for help from others without the need to feel guilty about it.'

When the boys noticed how I was being affected, they were insistent I should allow someone else to help out before I became too tired or too ill to be of any use to their dad. Eventually the workload reached a stage when I had to admit that I needed help to look after Keith. I took the decision to pay for someone to help out, someone who could help me care for Keith in his own home, and to help out with some of the jobs around the house.

I'd heard of people having to remortgage their homes to pay for the care of their loved ones. I must admit, having to turn to others for support does leave you feeling somewhat vulnerable – especially when you have to expose not only your finances but your emotions too. I'd been very reluctant for such a long, long time to have a carer move in.

Like most people, Keith and I enjoyed our privacy and I'd convinced myself that I'd be able to cope but, in the end, I just couldn't. I felt as if I was a failure, but I'd promised Keith right from the beginning that I'd keep him at home with me, that I'd take care of him. With all my background, and the help of our boys, I'd been sure we'd be able to do it. In the end, it was Juliet, Keith's Parkinson's nurse, who convinced me that I should seek extra help. 'If you walked out of the door today and got knocked over by a car, who would look after Keith?' she asked. 'He couldn't look after himself, you know.' I realised she was right.

Thinking about what Juliet had said I realised that, if I was not at home and Keith needed help urgently, he wouldn't have been able to use the telephone to call for assistance. He wouldn't be able to do so physically, nor would he know what to do, even how to dial a number. I realised I had to even think for Keith as well as myself. I was in a difficult situation. It was becoming obvious that Keith needed full-time care, yet I had a full-time ministry. I had to work in order to pay to support us both on a daily basis – to pay our bills. I felt I was in a Catch-22 situation.

Eventually the people arrived to assess the care required. They certainly knew their business. One of them was a financial expert who had trained as a counsellor. He was marvellous, a lovely man. Like Juliet, he was an incredible support who helped me to understand just how much help we needed. Another consideration the experts bear in mind is to how the person requiring care and their partner will get on with their new carer. It's a big step to have someone who is basically a stranger moving into your home.

Unfortunately, Keith loathed the first person we had! He just couldn't seem to bear the thought of having someone else in the house to take care of him. That's just not like Keith because Charlotte was absolutely lovely and, prior to his illness he would never have dreamed of thinking that way about someone. He had been so easy-going, and would happily get along with just about anyone. It's not as though Charlotte had had to give Keith intense personal care because, at that time, he was still able to take himself to the toilet. Charlotte was there just to help keep an eye on Keith and to help out with some of the domestic chores such as the ironing – jobs I'd been falling behind on while having to concentrate on my ministry.

Having a live-in carer also has extra costs – for a start there's an extra mouth to feed. But at least our home was large enough to accommodate another person, not everyone is so fortunate. Obviously, for some, this would not be an option. At one point we had carers coming in each morning to help Keith out of bed and dress him; helpers from a local charitable organisation, Tendring Crossroads, then came in for one morning and one afternoon before increasing the cover to two mornings and two afternoons as Keith deteriorated; and, when Keith began wandering at night, a night shift was arranged.

Keith began experiencing nightmares more frequently – he was so frightened all the time – it was horrible. One evening while we were holding a Parochial Church Council committee meeting in The Rectory garden Keith became convinced that the people there were coming to attack him. The nightmares in fact had begun long before Keith was diagnosed while I was working at St Jo's in 1995. The first signs were the twitching as he slept. Then he began to constantly throw himself around the bed each night. At first I'd been rather unsympathetic, 'Give me a night's sleep Keith, go and sleep in the other bed so I can sleep properly!'

The nightmares Keith was experiencing were truly horrible and it was distressing to lie there listening to him crying out in such turmoil and seeing him so anxious that I'd have to wake him up. Having said that, once he was awake he could rarely remember what he'd been dreaming about, other than saying 'I'm being chased! I'm being chased!' Naturally, both of us would be extremely tired the following day owing to such limited sleep and Keith's constant movement throughout the night.

Since we'd moved into The Rectory we often slept separately, even if only for part of the night. However, once Keith began to wander in the night, having him sleep in another room was too worrying so we moved a bed into the side of our large double bedroom near to a sink. We're told it was always necessary for rectories to have a very large bedroom with washing facilities just in case the bishop was to stay overnight – but that's something that never happened while we were there! However that extra room proved its worth to us.

Keith's bed was placed so that I could see him from where I was laying. Some nights he would sleep there, other nights he'd sleep with me. However, the nights became more and more restless and it came to a point where the decision was taken for us to sleep in separate beds most of the time.

Keith didn't seem to have recurring nightmares although there's one I have more cause to remember than most. This was the one I'd previously failed to mention to Giles, when I was woken by Keith's hands around my neck. Apparently, Keith had thought I was a piece of rope and he was trying to pull it tightly. He dreamt he was in a boat that had been moored to the side of a river. The river had been rising very quickly and Keith had been trying to keep the boat under control. He'd been trying to pull the boat into the riverbank but, unfortunately, he was using my neck to do so. To say it was a scary moment would be an understatement!

I've since been told there are people who can analyse dreams and some say that if someone dreams of a river it is supposed to symbolise their life, maybe a boat being the sign of one's journey through life. Poor Keith, things were beginning to change in his world and he just didn't understand what was going on.

Of course there were many occasions when Keith was unable to describe his nightmares at all. Sometimes he would wake up screaming in terror but things eased more in that respect as time went gone on. Sometimes he'd begin screaming but wouldn't wake at all. All I could do when that happened would be to hold him and try to reassure him that I was with him and that he was safe until he calmed down again. Night time wasn't the only time Keith suffered. He'd have waking dreams, hallucinations that caused him considerable distress. It must have been so scary for him but, Keith being Keith, he never once complained about his experiences. Like the time when he had field after field of trees to prune, he'd just get on with it.

Meanwhile, Andrew decided it would be a good idea to take Keith out for a ride. He picked him up and they headed off to a local golf club. Although Keith had never really played golf, Andrew thought that a ride around the course on a golf buggy would be a good opportunity to get Keith out of The Rectory for a while and allow him to get a breath of fresh air. He also had another motive.

'I thought it would be nice to give Dad the opportunity to hit a few balls,' Andrew recalls. 'Although this was not his game, the sporting prowess Dad had shown in his younger days hadn't completely deserted him despite his poor health – which was evident when he hit the ball straight on to the green! I'd been keen to get Dad on his own to have a private chat with him as I was concerned about his ability to carry on driving the car.

'As delicately as I could I suggested that maybe the time had come for him to consider giving up driving the car. I wondered how he would react but, just like Dad, he didn't get angry or upset. Maybe he'd already known the end of his driving days were fast approaching and, thankfully, he quietly accepted my advice. This was a very significant step for him; after all, he could only walk a very short distance by this time, and to agree to give up driving would mean accepting that he would have to give up a good deal of his own independence too.'

Andrew also recalls the visual hallucinations his father was experiencing at the time. 'Dad's hallucinations may have been frightening for him at times, but this was not always the case. Sometimes, when he was just sitting there 'writing in the air' with his hands, I would gently hold his hands to see if he would stop, but he firmly seemed to believe he really was seeing what he was 'seeing'. Sometimes he would vividly describe what he was 'seeing'.

'Once, there was a huge marquee in The Rectory's grounds. Dad was sitting inside the marquee, 'writing in the air' and describing to me the big brass band at the far end of the marquee (which wasn't really there at all). He calmly described the band to me in great detail. 'Dad', I said, 'you know it's not *really* there, don't you?' 'Oh yes, oh yes,' he replied, but not at all convincingly.

'Most of the times I was with Dad when he hallucinated I didn't get the feeling he was becoming frustrated or upset at 'seeing' things that were not really there. In fact, I was often of the impression that he was quite happy to describe what he thought he was seeing.

'Dad had such unpredictable switches – one minute he could be talking to you quite normally, the next he could be completely inside himself. Sometimes he'd be wiped out for days. Other times he would mouth words silently but just couldn't get out the words he really wanted to express. It was so frustrating for him – and to anyone else trying to understand him.'

I remember one night being very, very tired. I was totally exhausted and found myself crying and crying. I guess I was at rock bottom. Keith had been up three, four, five times a night to go to the toilet and I wasn't getting any sleep at all.

He'd wander around the house so I'd had to buy a baby gate to put across the stairway so he wouldn't fall down the stairs. Andrew's wife Kay persuaded me to go to a ballet dance class with her. Andrew would stay at our home overnight with Keith so I could go back to their home after the class to catch up on some much-needed sleep.

However, Andrew had also been out working hard all day and often had to bring work home with him so he too was very tired. Yet again, Keith was in and out of bed most of the night and Andrew was getting increasingly tired and eventually dropped off to sleep.

Soon afterwards, Keith managed to get out of bed once more and, without disturbing Andrew in the next room, he was able to undo the stairgate and made his way downstairs, out of the front door and began wandering down the road, somehow even managing to put a jumper on over his pyjamas. It's very fortunate The Rectory is in such a secluded lane which, apart from when there's a service in the church, sees very little traffic. Keith found himself in the car park opposite the church, which is only 50 to 100 metres away, but then realised he didn't know how to get home again. Anything could have happened to him. It's since made me realise how easy it is for someone to wander off and get lost while in a confused state as you often hear about on the news or read about in the newspapers.

Eventually Keith found his way to the church clerk's cottage, two doors away from The Rectory. At 4am he managed to wake up Angela who lives there. She must have been very surprised to open her front door and to find Keith standing in front of her in his pyjamas. It was fortunate she recognised him – Keith hadn't been outdoors very much for a long, long time. Thankfully, Angela and her husband brought Keith safely home to The Rectory. Poor Andrew – he'd been so tired that he hadn't even realised Keith had gone. That was the point when we realised that there would be no other option – we needed to obtain night care provision.

Social Services arranged for someone to care for Keith one night a week but this was increased to two nights, then three and so on. Yet Keith never again tried to wander off in the night. Whether psychologically he knew there was someone awake close at hand, or whether it was due to the night-time medication prescribed by Giles, I'm not sure. I do know though, that when Keith first began to take the medicine, it was sheer bliss! I used to joke that I needed it more than him. More importantly, it meant that for the first time in a very long time, Keith was able to get a decent night's sleep and that made a huge difference to him in the daytime, and his hallucinations became less frequent.

However, after a while I noticed Keith was deteriorating mentally. I sought further help from Giles. I asked if there was anything more he could do to help Keith. After a short hesitation Giles said: 'Well . . .

there's this drug called Exelon on the market, but it's very new and it's only been tried on patients with Alzheimer's. I suppose we could try it on Keith . . . but I don't know if it'll work.'

Exelon comes in tablet or patch form. Giles suggested that if we reduced the Sinemet dosage there might possibly be some benefit in experimenting with an Exelon/Sinemet combination with Keith. There seemed little to lose by giving it a go. The medication was prescribed, Keith began taking the combination of drugs and, believe it or not, suddenly I had my husband back! The transformation in Keith's health was absolutely miraculous, incredible! It was just as if someone had switched on a light in his brain.

For those readers who are caring for someone with this dreadful disease, the next few pages will, I hope, play a significant part in reassuring you if you have ever doubted whether or not the recipient of your care can appreciate or is aware of your efforts. If you've been wondering if your loved one, who seems to be in a world of his or her own, can really understand what you are saying to them – or if they really know who you are – I'm pretty sure I can reassure you that they do.

Within just 24 hours Keith was practically back to normal. That's the miracle for us. Almost immediately he stopped 'writing in the air' with his hands, the hallucinations stopped and he was able to tell me what the hallucinations had been like. He was alert, he could remember things again and, most importantly from my point of view, I knew he could remember who I was again! Keith had the most beautiful blue eyes but, when he was ill, they would become cloudy and distant. Suddenly his eyes went back to being piercing blue and he was looking at me again. Beforehand he wasn't really doing that. Normal interaction became possible:

'Would you like a cup of tea?'

'Yes please.'

We hadn't had this for ages. Normally I'd say 'Would you like a cup of tea, Keith?'

No response.

'Would you like a cup of tea?'

No response.

'Would you like half a cup of tea?'

Nothing. Not even a please or thank you. Keith had, seemingly, forgotten the social graces.

All the words that had been confusing him came flooding back into normal use and, better still, in the right order. There was not a sign of any confusion. You would never have believed how Keith had been just 24 hours earlier. It was a miracle!

I remember my astonishment when Keith first spoke to me: 'Keith, did I hear you right, did you just say that?'

'Say what?'

Then he'd repeat it, no problem. Overnight he knew again who I was, where I was, where he was in the house . . . everything! I noticed Keith's energy levels returning, his interest and zest for life. He was fine again and I just could not conceal my joy.

As soon as the combination of medication kicked in, it was obvious Keith knew exactly who he was, where he was, and what he was doing. Life returned to a greater degree of normality. Overnight I'd felt as if a huge burden had been lifted from my shoulders. I could leave Keith on his own, I could talk to him about things and get the appropriate responses. We made some decisions together again and our physical relationship was slightly better. He was fine! Naturally, the boys were also delighted to see the transformation in Keith's well-being.

Ben's recollections sum up his feelings at the time: 'It was overwhelming. Wonderful. Amazing. I'm not a believer in God. I didn't see it as miraculous – I guess I just saw it as a result of a mixture of medications all panning out to produce the appearance of a miracle.

'Everything about Dad that we'd assumed had been destroyed by his illness we now realised had not been destroyed after all. It was all there. He was back!

'Yet he couldn't see why I was welling up with tears. 'You're back!' I cried. Dad just looked at me as if to say 'well I haven't actually been away anywhere!' He could remember things that had been happening but I don't think he had the realisation of how he'd actually been at the time he was so ill. Clearly there were gaps in his memory so he couldn't work out why I was so emotional. It was as if he was thinking 'what's all the fuss about?'

'Dad had improved so dramatically and so fast. He seemed just as he had been five years earlier – it was that incredible. The hard thing was knowing that, although he was back, it was too good to last – he'd probably go downhill again sometime soon. I remember Mum often asking me if I felt this could last –  could Giles have found a cure? – although I'm sure she suspected deep down just as I did that it was a temporary respite.

'I tried to prepare Mum for the fact that Dad would probably deteriorate again sometime and that he may do so just as quickly as he had just improved. I guess we just had to be thankful that we'd witnessed a dramatic improvement in Dad's symptoms and that we should grasp the moments we had unexpectedly been given and savour them as much as we could. It was as if Dad had been given a reprieve.

'Realising that Dad had been aware of what had been going on around him made me rethink how I should behave while I was with him. While Dad seemed mentally distant I'd often sit with him to keep him company. It's dreadfully hard to think of something to say to someone who cannot respond so I'd often just sit there and read next to Dad or watch TV with him.

'Now, I realised, it was important to actually speak to him as if he were able to speak to me. From that point on, I told Dad about everything I could think of in my life because I was now sure he could understand what I was saying and that he would have wanted to feel he could share in my experiences.'

Simon was delighted to see the improved levels of his father's alertness: 'It was marvellous to see Dad responding verbally without any delays. His spirits were lifted, his general cheeriness was amazing. As far as his communication skills were concerned, he'd never really lost them – it's just that he couldn't express them – they were so far inside. Now he could enjoy speaking to us all again. It really lifted him – and us! The stoop he'd had disappeared. It was almost as if he was back to his old self. Although he'd gone downhill

Baby Keith Prestney and, below, in his school uniform.

Keith was a keen sportsman. He's seen here, sitting front left, a member of the victorious Inter-Departmental Cricket Competition held at the Royal Military Academy, Sandhurst in 1955.

Keith centre, back row, holds the shield after captaining the Young Conservative Club's hockey team to victory in the 1960s.

A very proud and happy day as the new Mr and Mrs Prestney
walk down the aisle on January 31, 1970.

Left: This picture was taken when our son Andrew was just six weeks old. I'd gone to sleep exhausted and, when I awoke, Keith had changed and fed him for the first time. Right: My ordination day. Keith was always supportive of my work in the church.

Left: Keith holds our grandson Jonathon. At this stage we were unaware Keith was at the very early stages of his illness. Right: At home on the land. I love this picture of Keith, taken just as we had sold Greshams Farm.

Just after his diagnosis of Parkinson's Disease, Keith joined me in Devon. Here he is seen admiring the roses, no doubt comparing them with those he had grown at home. At this time, Keith was not taking any medication.

Although ill, this photo shows Keith with a much-improved awareness of his surroundings while we were on holiday in France. At last I had my husband back so I rarely missed the opportunity of a much-needed cuddle!

Left: Eventually, the disease caught up with Keith. He was rarely well enough to enjoy a day out. Here, he's seen having a rest, but with a very vacant expression on his face.

Left: Keith could still occasionally feed himself in the earlier days of his illness, but it took some time. Right: This is the man to whom we owe so much – consultant neurologist Giles Elrington's combined prescription of Sinemet and Exalon played a huge part in extending and improving the quality of Keith's life.

74

Although he had been unwell, Keith looked fine as I was inducted at St Mary's Church, Lawford. We are pictured here with The Rt Revd Edward Holland, Bishop of Colchester.

Early on in his illness, Keith is seen here enjoying the company of our good friends Bob and Mary Ward while on holiday in France.

Looking pretty well, the medication, on a good day, could make it appear as though there was nothing wrong with Keith . . .

. . . but it was too good to last. The disease caught up with Keith again. And, during the final two and a half years of Keith's life, we could not have done without the help of 'Saint' Teresa.

so far it seemed to us as if he'd come back almost to where he was before.

'I remember being able to talk to Dad, knowing he could understand what I was saying. I truly believe Dad and I became even closer during this period. I wanted to grab the opportunity to make the most of the improvement as none of us were sure how long these moments would last. These moments were far too precious to waste.'

Although Keith had started on a low dose of Exelon, Giles had not been able to guarantee that anything positive would happen so Keith's improvement was greatly appreciated by all concerned. What was working for Keith may have had little or no effect at all on another patient. Keith was aware of how he had been prior to taking the combination of medicines. He realised that what he had 'seen', although it had been real to him, hadn't been real at all. 'I knew it wasn't real,' he said, 'but, nevertheless, it *was* there.'

Keith was able to tell us what he could understand, how he felt, before he was prescribed this combination of drugs. For instance, he would often throw the covers off the bed and talk incoherently as he did so. I asked him what had been going through his mind and he told me that there had been a little Italian girl sitting on the edge of the bed and that he was talking to her and telling her to go away. Where on earth did that come from I wondered. Then I remembered that when Keith and I were engaged we would often eat at an Italian restaurant in Colchester and there used to be a little Italian girl who would stand by our table and talk to us and I can only imagine that, somewhere deep down in Keith's consciousness, those memories were becoming intertwined with Keith's dreams.

Keith was also able to describe the times when he had appeared to be extremely frightened by something he had 'seen' in the room. I'd ask him 'what is it?' and he'd just keep repeating 'it's there, it's there!'

'Look at that cushion on the sofa,' said Keith. ' What can *you* see?' I told me I could see a cushion. 'Yes, but *what else* can you see?' asked Keith. 'Nothing,' I replied, 'other than some creases in the cushion'. 'Well,' explained Keith, '*I* could see a face – a very frightening face.' Then, when I looked at the cushion, I thought *you're right*! I could see what he meant. The shadows and creases combined, if you really thought about it, to appear like an angry face. For Keith though, this had been a reality.

He went on to describe how he was often convinced the room was filled with people, frightening people who really scared him, even though, in reality, there was no-one else there at all. Although our dog Sam had died, Keith described how he had often crossed the room and had stepped over Sam very carefully and deliberately – it's just that Sam wasn't there.

Now, in his more lucid state, Keith was opening a door to let us in to what had been going on in his sometimes frightening, confused world. Now, at last, we were getting a privileged glimpse of life as it had been for Keith at a time when communication between us had been so difficult. Thrilled as the boys and I were, I think we realised this state of affairs would, most likely, be too good to last for long. However, I was delighted to be presented with another window in time to be with Keith.

Giles had warned us that the combination of medicines may not work at all, in which case there would be nothing more he could do about it as he did not normally prescribe this combination for Diffuse Lewy Body Disease. This particular combination was usually only offered, at the time, to people with Alzheimer's Disease. Giles had hoped we might get a few good weeks, possibly months and, guardedly, he mentioned years but, as this treatment had rarely been tried with someone with Diffuse Lewy Body Disease, he really had no idea of how successful it may be.

We were just so very fortunate that Giles was prepared to take a chance to see how the combination might help Keith. He had the expertise to know that this was a course of action worth trying out. Exelon has a side effect of making the patient feel very sick but, again, we were fortunate that, with Keith, this only lasted for around three or four days. We soon realised that Keith had become much more able to express his feelings and his language skills improved significantly. Basically, he just blossomed.

I found it most reassuring that what I had been doing to help Keith, although I hadn't known it at the time, had been appreciated. Now he was able to tell me what had been helpful to him and what had not. He was at pains to reassure me he was happy with everything I'd done to help him. That was a huge relief to me because when someone is unable to communicate with you, you don't know for sure if you're doing the right thing in their eyes.

Having Keith 'come back' to us was absolutely wonderful and it made me realise how fortunate I was to have the opportunity to hear from him how he felt about our efforts to make him more comfortable. There are so many carers out there who would give their eye teeth for some sign that their loved ones realise that what they are trying to do is appreciated, that the sufferer is aware of who they are and of what they are doing.

Hopefully, this part of our story will go some way to reassure those of you who have found yourselves in a similar situation. It's so easy to think that, because someone can't respond to you, they can't receive the signals you are offering them. It would be easy to slip into a way of talking about them in front of them as if they are not there at all. I have to admit, I've done that myself from time to time. It's the 'does he take sugar?' syndrome, where one can forget that although the person who has difficulty in communicating is present, they may well understand what is going on around them. It's not just in cases like Keith's but with people who have been badly injured in accidents or have brain tumours and such like.

There are all sorts of brain damage conditions where one should just assume that the patient really is still the same person deep down inside and that everything they ever thought when they were well, everything that they found amusing or upset or angered them, is still likely to do so now. Those signals may still be going in, it's just that they can't express their feelings.

Like his brothers, Andrew was ecstatic at his father's improvement. 'It was as if someone had switched the lights back on. I experienced feelings of great joy when Dad was able to describe lucidly how much he had been able to understand and what his experiences had been. This was a lifeline, a small miracle of science,' he recalled, 'that's why I truly believe in the importance of treating someone like Dad when they are not able to communicate themselves as you would if they were well. Just because someone cannot respond it doesn't mean they cannot take in information and process it on an emotional level. It's just that they cannot express themselves outwardly.'

In the early stages of Keith's illness he would laugh out loud most inappropriately. He'd suddenly start laughing hilariously, at times, almost like a maniac – and he couldn't stop himself. It became most embarrassing whenever it happened, but he had no control over it. Something would just trigger the emotion in him. It could have been something he'd seen on television, or a memory, and I often found myself having to apologise on his behalf, explaining to people that my husband had a form of Parkinson's Disease and that his laughter was out of his control. I had to reassure them that Keith hadn't been laughing at them. With this much welcomed mental improvement, I took the opportunity to ask him one day why he had laughed out so often and he simply replied, 'because I couldn't cry'.

We were determined to make the most of Keith's improvement in health. Bearing in mind he loves nothing more than a good holiday, I booked a trip on a cruise liner around the Mediterranean Sea. Who'd have thought it, after all we'd gone through, here I was booking up a Mediterranean cruise – absolutely unbelievable! We flew out to Palma, then sailed across to Morocco, where we went on coach trips and dances, and onwards on the ship from there. Everything was more or less 'normal' and we were having a most wonderful time. Keith was thoroughly enjoying himself, though I must admit he was feeling more tired than usual, but that should probably have been expected as we were packing in quite a lot each day.

There were one or two moments when things didn't go quite to plan and other moments when slight signs of Keith's condition became apparent. He's never been one for making quick choices but, while we were on the ship we sat at the same table for our meals with the same people each day and, sometimes, Keith would spend absolutely ages choosing what he wanted to eat from the menu – and, of course, nobody was served until everyone had made their choices. To counteract this, I helped him to cut down the choices: 'Look Keith, you don't like haddock and you don't like chicken curry so what's left is roast beef or grilled plaice. Would you like roast beef or grilled plaice?' That usually helped, but it still left a choice of two dishes!

Yes, we had a wonderful holiday, but that was only until the last day of the cruise when Keith had a stomach upset and, suddenly, he couldn't keep his tablets down and this resulted in him going into a rapid downward spiral. Suddenly confusion and stiffness reigned. His mobility suffered dramatically and he became very dizzy. I hurried off to seek help from the nursing sister on the ship and asked for her to come to our cabin to check Keith over before the flight home. Meanwhile, back in our cabin, Keith was repeatedly being sick and, because of his confusion, he was unable to reach the toilet in time which, as you can imagine, made for a lot of messy clearing up. The sister gave Keith an injection to counter the sickness which, fortunately, had an almost instant effect.

Boosted by this, I felt somewhat reassured as we boarded the budget flight home to England. Our seats were to the back of the plane, close to the toilets so I guess that made me feel more confident that Keith would be all right throughout the flight. Thankfully, we arrived home without further incident and, once Keith had been able to keep his medication down once more, things improved significantly. However, our holiday had proved beyond doubt the fragility of Keith's physical and mental states and how our reliance on this rare medical combination could not be taken for granted.

That said, once we had settled back to normal day-to-day life, Keith was perky and lucid again and we continued to enjoy our lives once more. Things were pretty good now and I was happy to see how well Keith was doing and how he was able once more to do the things he had been totally unable to do a few months previously.

We were determined to enjoy these moments to the maximum while we could. We knew we were probably on borrowed time. I'm so very grateful to Giles for telling us what it could be like towards the end of Keith's life. 'Seize the moment,' he'd advised us, and that's one of the main messages I would like to pass on in this book. Seize the moment, because you never know when the opportunity may pass you by or whether it will ever return. It would be so easy to let everything make you wholly miserable, to let everything close in on you, to give up.

Giles had been reasonably confident that the combination of medications would be likely to help Keith although, he added, that with any individual patient with any treatment you know they cannot always respond according to the average. He had already tried this combination on other patients but, with Keith, he believed the dramatic success of the combination was partly down to the fact that Keith was a man who tended to take the attitude that the glass was half full. Giles told us that a lot of patients have a different attitude towards life and their illnesses, and it seemed some often wished he could give them a jab of something to make their illness go away and hoped that was the end of it.

Giles was pleased that Keith had responded better to the dosage of Sinemet than he had hoped. 'I had been concerned that the drug could have upset his mental state – as it can do,' he told us, adding: 'One of the paradoxes that you face when treating both Parkinsons and Lewy Body Disease, is that you have two different neuro-chemical abnormalities. The movement disorder you find in both cases is caused by a shortage of the chemical dopamine which can be addressed by administering drugs based upon L-Dopa like Sinemet and, if you give a big enough dose of that often enough I find that works really well.

'In the short to medium term the effects are generally not that great. There is also the non-motor or cognitive part of the illness which affects probably everyone in time. This reflects a different chemical abnormality – a shortage of the neurotransmitter acetylcholine. The more dopamine-related drugs you take, the worse you make the non-motor symptoms and so, very often, you have to soft pedal the movement disorder in order to maintain the cognitive levels.

'Basically, you're faced with a choice between a mobile and cognitively-impaired patient versus an immobile, cognitively-intact patient. In my view that's no real choice, I'd always aim for the latter.

'All treatments carry an element of risk – there's no drug that's so powerful that it gives benefits to anyone without upsetting others.

My particular concern with Keith was that by treating his movement disorder I might worsen his cognition. Thankfully though he was brave enough to go ahead with the treatment and everything improved.

'The combination of Sinemet and Exelon is now one I regularly administer to patients with Diffuse Lewy Body Disease. We all have our own ways of treating patients – and all sorts of different views regarding treatment – but, fundamentally, the issue is whether you rely on Leva Dopa preparations such as Sinemet or whether you go for the other drugs. I feel very strongly that other drugs have a great risk of upsetting cognition, though a lot of other doctors will do what I think is a very 1990s practice of using everything but Leva Dopa or Sinemet until they really have to. I guess I just have to accept that there are different ways to skin a rabbit.

'At the end of the day, neither Sinemet or Exelon are expensive treatments – the real expense is the personal care aspect of the disease.'

# THE BUBBLE BURSTS

Behind all this joy and our new lease of life, Diffuse Lewy Body Disease was invisibly yet relentlessly strengthening its grip on Keith – it had not finished with him yet – not by a long, long way. Slowly but surely, the miracle cure showed signs of subsiding and Keith's medication had to be adjusted to compensate for the regression. I guess it had been several months since Keith's meteoric return to normality began but, gradually, he was slipping back into a more confused and unstable state.

It was heartbreaking stuff. We knew we were on borrowed time and we were determined to make the most of things before this dreadful disease regained the upper hand. Giles had explained to Keith that whatever the medication did for him, it would only offer a window in time, it could not totally stop the progression of the disease. It might give him a month, or even another six months of normality, it just wasn't possible to give an exact prognosis.

Months passed into a year and all in the Prestney household, thanks to the occasional adjustments in Keith's medication, ensured that life on the whole was pretty good, so good in fact that I booked another holiday, this time a self catering trip to Majorca.

Prior to our departure I decided that, although Keith had taken a slight dip healthwise, he was quite well enough for another foreign adventure. How wrong I was! With the airline I'd selected, if you pre-booked with someone who needed help, they could provide a wheelchair and help you fast track through the terminal at the airport. We were offered seats at the front of the plane near the toilets. However, the flight out there totally disorientated Keith. When it came to serving up the flight meals I found myself having to choose what I wanted and also having to choose for Keith.

Then Keith decided he wanted to go to the loo. I got up with Keith and led him to the toilet door. The toilet wasn't large enough for us both to go in at the same time so I told Keith I'd wait for him just outside the door.

'Now then, Keith, whatever you do, DON'T lock the door.'

Keith went in.

'Keith, DON'T lock the door . . . Keith, can you hear me? I'm standing right outside waiting for you.'

I could hear Keith doing what he had to do, then heard him flush the toilet. I remember thinking to myself, oh, I do hope he remembers to do his trousers up before he comes out!

Then I heard it . . . CLICK. Keith had locked the door. He'd locked himself in the loo and I knew he would not be able to work out how to get out on his own. Meanwhile, a queue of passengers waiting for the toilet was forming behind me.

'Keith, turn the lock.'

'What lock? There isn't a lock.'

'Yes there is darling, it's just in front of you . . . just turn it to the right.'

Some time passed as this conversation went round and round in circles. We were getting nowhere and the queue behind me was increasing. There was nothing for it, I had to find someone able to open the door to extricate Keith. I hurried to the rear of the plane where the hostesses were still serving meals. 'I'm terribly sorry to bother you, but my husband's got rather muddled and he's just shut himself in the toilet, can you help me get him out?' Fortunately, they had a key especially for the exterior lock of the door and Keith was duly rescued.

From that point on, our holiday just went downwards. Keith's confusion rose to the point that he didn't know who I was, which was quite frightening. As a precaution I wrote on a piece of paper '*My name is Keith Prestney, I am residing at . . . . this is my wife's mobile telephone number*'. I couldn't risk Keith and I becoming separated at any point, he just wouldn't have been able to cope at all.

We were blessed with some really sunny weather during this break but, during the afternoons, all Keith could do was sleep. He was so, so tired. Normally, I would have had a job stopping Keith from going into the resort's swimming pool, such was his love of the water. Like me, he would rarely be out of a pool. Now, however, whenever he entered the pool he seemed to feel, literally, out of his depth even when he was standing in the shallow end of the pool. He didn't seem to have any co-ordination at all.

One night, at bedtime, I sat Keith down onto the bed ready to help him undress. He began to get upset, 'I can't do this, I can't do this,' he said. 'It's alright darling, of course you can,' I reassured him, but Keith was adamant, 'no, no, no, my Patsy wouldn't like it!' he cried. 'But, darling, I *am* Patsy,' I said. 'No, no, no, I can't do this, Patsy wouldn't like it!' Poor Keith, he actually thought I was someone else, maybe some other woman trying to seduce him. In one way, it was rather lovely that Keith was trying to be so loyal to me by pushing away the unwanted attentions of 'another woman', but, on the other hand, it was very, very sad because, at that moment he had no idea of who I was and I found that very frightening, particularly as we were so far away from home. It was at this point I realised that I couldn't even leave Keith alone in a room, even for a short period of time. I'd have to take him absolutely everywhere with me – even to the loo.

We knew when Giles prescribed the Exelon that there was a maximum dose. As Keith deteriorated, the dose was increased but the negative effect of this was that Keith's mobility was impaired. It was inevitable that at some point the drugs would only go so far, that we'd reach the point where the dosage could not be increased any further. Every time the dosage was increased we were aware of the fact that we were getting nearer to the end of the road as far as this particular course of medication was concerned. That was a horrible experience which occurred four times. Each time Keith improved slightly then gradually slipped back again. The improvement could last weeks, sometimes months but, every time, the combination of drugs began to wear off.

The deterioration in Keith's condition was a very gradual process, so gradual that, thankfully, he was totally unaware of it. His mental and physical state had constantly risen and fallen so there was no really clear-cut point that I can recall when I could have appreciated how much more time he would have before his dosage would need to be increased. We faced that uncertainty every minute of every day and that's really difficult to live with. For some time we struggled to find a suitable balance of medication that would prolong Keith's mental and mobility improvements. We had to accept that these drugs do not work in the same way for everybody. We'd been grateful that, at least for Keith, the results had been absolutely wonderful, miraculous – in fact, he'd been almost back to his old self.

As the boys and I noticed Keith regressing we experienced a sense of grieving. It was as if, each day, he was dying a little more, that he was gradually leaving us again. Having Keith being able to express his thoughts and feelings had given us a short but privileged insight into his secret, parallel world. It made me realise I could sit in the same room as Keith at the same time, yet we'd be experiencing totally different surroundings. By now Keith was experiencing neurological changes that were affecting his bladder control and he was becoming incontinent at times throughout the day and night. He was no longer able to dress or undress himself, or go to the toilet unaided.

This must have been particularly embarrassing for Keith – everyone, even when they are ill, has some dignity they wish to retain – but because of Keith's confusion, he found it difficult to remember where the toilet was to be found. The whole situation was a very gradual, gentle process. First of all, as the toilet door and my study door were practically side by side, I stuck a picture of a woman sitting at a desk on my door and a gentleman's toilet sign on the other so he could recognise which door he needed. Then things deteriorated to a stage when I'd have to ask Keith if he needed any help, maybe to undo his trousers or to sit him down on the loo. He began to rely on me more and more at these times and that's when I realised I was beginning to be as much Keith's carer as I was his wife. My role was changing.

Giles explained that Keith was now in the palliative stage of his illness and that 'all we can hope for is to keep cognition as long as we can – once muscle control begins to go, as is evidenced by his bladder problems, then other muscles and the autonomic system will also shut down'. My guess at this point was that we were probably looking at months rather than years before Keith would no longer know who I was or would be able to keep movement or cognition.

The parallels between our story and the film *Awakenings*, which starred Robin Williams, are quite amazing. This film was based on the work of Dr Oliver Sacks who, while working at a hospital in The Bronx, New York in 1969, experimented with a new drug to treat catatonic patients. Basically, in the early 1900s, an epidemic of encephalitis lethargica spread worldwide. Symptoms included tremors, muscle pains, a slowing of physical and mental response and drowsiness. Sufferers displayed Parkinson's Disease-like symptoms.

Around five million people were killed by causes related to this dreadful disease while others slipped into a catatonic state which lasted for decades. Dr Sacks had been fascinated by these people and decided to try an experimental course of treatment to see if he could help lift them from their catatonic state. He proposed that a new drug known as Levodopa (L-Dopa) should be used as a treatment for one of his catatonic patients and, before long, the patient was displaying signs of recovery.

Dr Sacks extended the treatment to other sufferers and they too displayed similar improvements until virtually all of them made complete recoveries. This sensational experiment took the medical world by storm and hopes were high of a permanent cure. However, just like with Keith, the effects of the medication subsided. Sadly, the human body develops a tolerance of L-Dopa which makes its effectiveness temporary and, one by one, Dr Sacks' patients slipped back into their catatonic states.

The pressure of caring for Keith and my ministry had accumulated to such a point I felt the need to write to my boss, Bishop Christopher, to explain the situation to him. I wrote that I had recently buried five people who lived in the area who had been diagnosed with the same condition as Keith, and that Keith's doctors were astounded that Keith was still with us at all. I asked if it would be possible to take two or three months off as compassionate leave after Christmas to give me the opportunity to look after Keith more effectively. I told the Bishop that I would have a better idea come the end of this period of whether I could pick up the reins and carry on once more or whether I should have to give up the parish altogether.

An added worry was that our home, The Rectory, would have to be vacated should I need to give up my work. In my letter I told the

Bishop we would have to look for a retirement property in the village for such an event. Fortunately, Bishop Christopher was most sympathetic to our plight and he responded by allowing me to take three months off from the beginning of January. With the support of retired clergy and the gifted and competent people who attend St Mary's Church in Lawford, services would be uninterrupted while I took time off with Keith.

But before my compassionate leave began, on November 11, 2006 – Remembrance Day – as I was getting ready for the church parade, I had a most terrible fright. Our boys would take turns to look after Keith while I worked, otherwise we'd have carers in. I took Keith to the toilet and he seemed fine. Then, just as I lifted him from the seat, he suddenly just slumped down on to the floor. I knew this was one of the defining features of Keith's illness, but it still came as a great shock. Basically, when he stood up, his blood pressure had dropped suddenly, causing him to collapse.

To be honest, I thought he'd gone, that Keith had died. At first he was totally out of it, no responses at all, then, thankfully, he showed signs of coming round. Simon and Jonathon were home so I called them to help me. Somehow we got Keith into his chair in the lounge and he seemed to improve. Meanwhile, there was a church full of people waiting for me. Once I was sure Keith was going to be okay with the boys, I hurried over to the church where I had been due to share the service with the Rev Paul Mann. I got through the service – somehow – but it was very difficult to concentrate on the proceedings knowing what had just happened to Keith.

Now was the time to come to a tough decision. Keith had to decide whether or not to keep the Exelon going so he could maintain some thought processes. He still knew who we were, but should he lose that to retain a greater degree of physical movement? We discussed this at great length over Christmas 2006 – the first Christmas we'd ever spent alone in The Rectory. I lit the fire and planned a romantic evening. I sat with my head on Keith's knee as we chatted about the options. It was a really, really tough conversation to engage in but Keith was quite 'with it' enough at the time to tell me what he would prefer. He recognised that things had been changing for the worse.

He thought they did so 'every six months' but then we spoke of how things had been changing rather more rapidly recently and how we had been able to control things with the medication but had reached a point where that was no longer possible.

We discussed whether it would be better for him to be more alert and less mobile or the other way around. Basically, he had to choose the lesser of two evils. Keith decided he would rather stay with us mentally and know who we were – even if that meant he would have to pay the price of his mobility. After our heart-rending discussion Keith eventually chose to lose some of his mobility by reducing his intake of Sinemet. This would reduce his confusion.  Once that decision had been made, it was still very tempting some days to give him less Exelon but we knew what would happen, particularly as we ran out of the medication one day. Before long, Keith didn't know anything at all. He could hardly breathe, he couldn't speak in any way – he couldn't communicate in any way at all.

Keith had told me that his greatest fear would be that he would end up in a care home and I was at pains to reassure him that I would do my utmost to ensure that would never happen – I would care for him at home. We talked about the fact that this would quite likely be our last Christmas together and how sad that made us feel – but also how many good times we had seen in the last seven years, a much longer time than the original prognosis. I recognised that I was grieving deeply for Keith.

There was a part of me that was longing for the boys to be here with us, to see us through the Christmas period, but the greater part of me wanted to set them free. I was saddened about all that Keith and I would never do together again, yet was mightily relieved that we had found the time to talk things through. Part of me was praying the Lord would take Keith quickly and easily, while another part of me was trying not to imagine life without him. I was beginning to learn the humility of not being 'needed'. We had been fortunate to enjoy short windows of time – and what wonderful moments they had been. So many people don't have those, so I guess we were blessed.

The reduction of Sinemet had awful effects. Keith would begin to shake from head to toe and he would experience moments of extreme weakness akin to the feeling you might expect just before you faint. Therefore, there were times when he could not even go outside the front door but, whenever it was at all possible, I would tell him, 'come on, we're going out today' – even if it was only for a short car ride or to park up on the seafront. Seizing the moment and making the most of really precious time together, that's what it was all about.

I decided that a visit to one of Keith's favourite places would be just the stimulus he needed. We were making the most of an improved period of his health by spending a few days in Norfolk. Seizing the moment. Keith had often spoken fondly in the past of his happy days at the private boarding school Greshams in Holt, the school he named the farm after. As we were in the vicinity I decided to drive there to take Keith on a journey down Memory Lane. The visit did Keith the world of good. After popping into the office and explaining my husband was rather poorly and that he was a former pupil, we were invited to wander around the school freely at our leisure. Many childhood memories came back and Keith really enjoyed showing me where his old dorm was, and the science laboratory and sports field. It was wonderful to see the pleasure Keith gained from our visit.

That was during a good phase of Keith's health but, unfortunately, these periods became fewer and fewer. It had been 12 months since Keith had collapsed when, suddenly, I saw the colour drain from his face once more. 'Oh-oh, he's gonna go!' I was just in time to lower him down on to the loo seat before he passed out completely. I managed to get him down on to the floor but then Keith started fitting and making terrible noises. Then he lay still, but still making those dreadful noises as he was struggling to catch his breath. I remember thinking: 'Please God, don't let it end like this'.

Then Keith's carer Lorraine appeared. 'Quickly, call for an ambulance!' I yelled, then seeing Keith completely motionless, I added: 'Don't worry, it's too late, he's gone.' I honestly thought I'd lost him. Then, suddenly, Keith began to come round again. I was *so* relieved. We let him lie on the floor for a while longer then managed to get him to his bed. The previous time he had collapsed, Keith had been sitting down and talking. What he was saying made sense, but it wasn't sense in a real way. What he was coming out with was totally irrelevant to the moment. This time, however, I recognised the signs and was able to get him to his bed before any real harm was done.

# A LONELY PLACE

One aspect of Keith's condition was that it was very isolating. Some people just didn't seem to know what to say to him if they didn't get a response from him. They either spoke very loudly at him, as if he was hard of hearing, which he wasn't, or they assumed he didn't know what they were talking about and discussed him in front of him. Others talked down to him, rather than talking normally to him. And, most sadly, a lot of friends simply stopped coming to see him. Because we couldn't go out, there were a lot of friends we didn't see any more. That hurt so much.

There were some friends who, I would have hoped, would have stuck with it far more than they did. When I was out and about and I saw them, they'd ask 'How's poor old Keith? We must come and see him sometime' but they didn't. But then, to be fair, although Keith played masses of sports when he was younger, he was never the person who would ring up a friend and say 'let's go out for a drink'. That just wasn't Keith's way.

His life was us, his family. Having said that, he would always be more than happy to go out with friends if they had made the initial approach, so I guess I can understand why some people would maybe not have remembered to come over to see him. And, of course, people have their own problems and lives to lead. Often people told me how much they'd been thinking about Keith and ask how we were coping and I found myself thinking, well, thinking is fine, but it would be much nicer to see you, especially as Keith really loved it when friends visited him.

We couldn't go out for dinner easily because eating in public was very difficult for Keith and I just couldn't put him through that any more. We just could not guarantee that Keith could actually sit at a table and eat a meal without his food going all over the table. That was embarrassing for Keith – even if other people didn't mind, Keith did.

Andrew has clear recollections of such times: 'When Dad struggled to eat or to swallow, well, that was a real low point for us as a family. As his condition went up and down we could sometimes find ourselves doubting what we had seen the previous day. Were we imagining things? Sometimes we needed someone to reassure us that Dad had indeed been able to do this or that the day before. It's a common theme for carers coping with people with conditions such as Dad's because you become so immersed in the situation you find yourself in. When someone's condition fluctuates so dramatically and so often it can be quite confusing when you try to pinpoint how they were at any given point of time. Mum's right, Dad's condition was isolating for her and the family and there was no-one in the parish who could really share or fully understand her experiences. As a result I guess you could say The Rectory became a 'protected stronghold'.'

Obviously Keith couldn't sit through a theatre performance – he just lost the thread of the storyline and started fidgeting and trying to get out of his seat. He couldn't cope with the cinema any more because there were too many visual images coming at him all at once. So what could we do? Where could we go? Apart from being with our family, there was not much else we could do.

Sometimes there could be something on the television that he would hear and he would be 'in' that situation. It would be real to him. For instance, if he heard that the price of apples had dropped, he would be worrying about his own apples going to market, even though he no longer had any apples to worry about. But for Keith, that was such a real thing and he could stress himself out over it.

Whenever I went out to work on my ministry or go shopping, I always prepared Keith for my departure. I had to reassure him of where I was going and for how long, almost like one would with a small child. Often he could be absolutely fine when I left but when I phoned home to check on him, his carer would tell me that he'd been totally confused all over again. There was no way of knowing how each day would pass.

Some days Keith forgot the most simple day-to-day things. Maybe he'd forget how to swallow, or how to go to the loo – or even how not to go to the loo. These were the things we could see. Sometimes he couldn't even remember how to get into bed. It sounds ridiculous.

After all, how hard could that be? There were times when I got frustrated with Keith. Getting him to bed, telling him *how* to get into bed. When I say I got frustrated *with* Keith, I suppose I mean I got frustrated *for* him. Things shouldn't have been like that. He should have been enjoying his life far more, enjoying his retirement.

So, we adopted a routine, which we always stuck to. The carers would have done this for me but I liked to think of this routine as *our* time. I'd take Keith to the kitchen and we got him a glass of water and his box of tablets. We'd then switch off the light and I'd lead him by the hand to the stairs. 'Up the stairs, darling', I'd say three or four times, 'keep going'. Most nights, halfway up the stairs, he'd stop and I'd have to remind him, 'keep going'.

At the top of the stairs he'd turn to go into the carer's room so I'd steer him towards the bathroom instead. 'We're going to clean your teeth now, Keith'. He would pick up a bottle or some aftershave so I'd have to remind him he needed a toothbrush instead. I'd have to take the toothbrush out of the pot and put the toothpaste on the brush for him.

Often he'd then try to put more toothpaste on the brush. I'd have to remind him that I'd already done that and tell him to run water over his toothbrush, but he'd get the taps muddled up and I'd have to help him to find the cold tap.

Once that was done, he'd usually remember how to clean his teeth and he'd spend absolutely ages doing so. While he was doing that, I'd find his pyjamas and turn back his bed. I'd return to the bathroom and he'd still be brushing his teeth. I'd then fill a tumbler with water so he could rinse his mouth.

He'd then spend ages drying his hands on just about anything but the towel. Then I'd guide him to the toilet and sit him down. Then I'd get him undressed and take off his glasses. I'd guide him through to the bedroom. Once there he'd remember he had to do something but had little idea what it might be.

I'd put a hairbrush in his hand and he'd try to brush his hair. I'd then pass him his tablet and remind him how to swallow it with a sip of water. I'd sit him on the edge of his bed and remove his slippers. I'd tell him to get into bed but he'd stand up and then start off walking around the room. I'd have to guide him again. 'It's time to get into bed, darling.'

Eventually, I'd get him sitting on the edge of the bed and encourage him to lift his feet up. Keith always slept on his right side so I'd have to turn him accordingly unless he was having a really good night when he could remember to do so himself. I'd tuck a pillow under his head and, inevitably, this was the moment he'd remember he wanted to tell me something, just as a child who didn't want to go to sleep would do. I think it was Keith's way of keeping me with him just a little longer. More often than not, he'd be so confused by this point I could rarely make head or tail of what he was talking about. I'd reassure him I'd sort out whatever was bothering him, give him a kiss and tell him to go to sleep.

All this took anything from 30 to 45 minutes and, when I was really tired myself, it seemed to take forever. It was so frustrating and just one more thing that made me grieve every night. Usually, by 8pm I'd be exhausted but, often at about 9pm I'd start to wake up. I got a surge of energy. That's when I found myself sitting alone in my study working until one or two o'clock in the morning. That was *my* time. It was when I was at my most creative.

Keith's best man Louis Thorp was very good. The day after Keith was diagnosed with Diffuse Lewy Body Disease Louis and his wife Jane, by pure chance, visited the church and found me in there in tears. When I told them how Giles had explained what life would be like for Keith. Louis, who lives locally, promised that they would regularly come to visit us, as did another friend David Butcher.

Louis and David were true to their word. They regularly visited and would take Keith out and about. For Keith, these were rare moments of normality – until that is, his condition deteriorated to such a degree that it wasn't possible to venture outside our home any longer.

At least though, Louis and David remained regular visitors, and I know Keith loved it when they called in because they treated him normally while enjoying a cup of coffee and reminiscing about old times. He was totally with them, he knew exactly what they were saying – even though he could not always respond as much as he would have liked to. These were truly lovely 'normal bloke' moments for Keith, which otherwise very rarely occurred for him.

We were blessed with some wonderful support, and I can't stress enough just how important that was for us – both the paid-for support and the friendships we made since Keith had been ill; believe me, we needed that so much because Keith's illness, as I've already mentioned, can be so isolating.

Sometimes I was asked how difficult it was to switch off, particularly if I'd been having a tricky day with Keith. How hard was it to put on a brave face before conducting a church service? Well, to be honest, there were times when I could not help but take my worries with me, but I tried so hard not to let anyone else realise it. After all, it was not their burden. Basically, I was there to do a job.

Nevertheless, there were people who worked alongside me in the church who I couldn't fool, people who knew me really, really well. I guess they could see it in my face if I'd been having a difficult or stressful day. Our friends Sue Jones, Susie Hyman and Mary Nunn saw Keith through all the different phases and that's probably why they understood how I was feeling on many a day. Then there were other people who thought they knew, but they didn't, and that was fine, and then there were others who just came over to me and gave me a hug.

Often there were times when I had to just take a deep breath, but that was my profession – I had to do what I had to do, there are expectations of a priest. When I took three months off, compassionate leave, I really desperately needed that space. I'd got to the stage where I'd just buried five people who had suffered a comparable illness to Keith in a very short space of time.

I'd noticed that life, particularly as far as Keith's health was concerned, had seemed to bump along on a level reasonably okay for ages, and then there was a moment when everything took a big dip and things never seemed to come back as high as they had been earlier.

I noticed that quite often people would die on the days when we didn't have carers in to help with Keith and there were often times when I was needed to conduct a funeral service at the local crematorium in Weeley when I had no option other than to take Keith with me. I'd then need to leave him in the car throughout the service having emphasised to him the necessity for him to stay there, not to wander off. Then I'd lock him in the car until I got back. Often, I'd ask the funeral directors or pall bearers, who were outside during the service, to keep an eye on Keith for me. That was a nightmare and it wasn't fair on Keith – nor was it particularly safe.

I remember one December day when I was called to conduct a funeral in the nearby village of Little Bentley where, years earlier, I had been a Reader. I found this particular day more than a little stressful. The nature of the deaths leading up to these funerals was far too close to home, bearing in mind Keith's illness. But, in the darkness of that day, one light shone through. Saul Hunnaball, the funeral director that day who knows me quite well, had noticed that, while the mourners were filing past the grave, I had taken myself quietly to one side.

'Are you all right Pat?' Saul asked. 'I can't do this any more, Saul. I can't do any more funerals, it's like burying my husband every time because I know that time is going to come. Everyone knows it.' Out of sight of the mourners I began to weep. I have to say, Saul, despite being very busy that day, was a huge support to me, and that remains very much appreciated.

There's no denying the isolation one can feel when the role of carer falls upon their shoulders. Even when help is received, there are still times when you find yourself on your own with your loved one. At times like these I found that reading the following poem, written by a good friend's relation, summed up my feelings:


**It is a Lonely Place (Caroline Toll 1999)**

*It is a lonely place*
*To know the suffering of another*
*To see the face*
*and know part is no longer there.*

*It is a lonely place*
*To cry in the night*
*With no comfort in loss*
*Or half a life.*

*It is a lonely place*
*To be in constant touch*
*To be demanded*
*By an endless need.*

*It is a lonely place*
*To have anxiety always*
*That care is there*
*When away from home.*

*It is a lonely place*
*To feel impatience*
*Outstripping love*
*and concern diminishing.*

*It is a lonely place*
*To look at the sky*
*and feel bound*
*Heart and foot.*

*It is a lonely place*
*To know no explanation*
*Can make sharing*
*Even a possibility.*

*It is a lonely place*
*To love and grieve*
*To live and half die*
*To feel fury and compassion.*

*It is a lonely place*

*To live in*
*and he too*
*That cannot speak.*

Meanwhile, everything in Simon's life had been falling apart. Not only was his father really ill, he went bankrupt, lost his job and his home, his relationship with Louisa had ended so badly that he was only able to see his son Jonathon at weekends and he was still having to live with us. To make matters worse, I realised he was taking drugs and had become depressed to the point of feeling suicidal. The depression he was experiencing proved exhausting for him and I hardly knew which way to turn in order to help him. Poor Simon was in a very lonely place. Sometimes he'd just lie on the sofa and sleep and sleep and sleep.

He recalls: 'I was really missing Jonathon. For nine months he had been living with me, now he was back living with Louisa as her health had improved enough for her to look after him again. I know I should have been more of a support to Mum but, at the time, I was going through a bitter period in my own life. I'd lost my home and my son. My faith had left me and I was involved in a custody battle over Jonathon. Missing my family unit, I met up with friends and spent far too much time socialising. After losing my job I chose drugs to escape my misery and that led to an even more dramatic downward spiral in my life. In the end I wasn't lucid enough – because of the drugs – to fully appreciate the difficulties Mum was facing.'

A friend, Barry Young, managed to find Simon a role in the church youth club. Simon went with Barry to help out at an organisation known as Big Bubble and that's where Simon met his future wife Michelle. Yes, Simon's got a story of his own to tell, though I'm pleased to say that, with Michelle's support, he has now turned his life around, having beaten all his demons, and he's become a committed Christian. The change in him has been immense and he's now happily married and able to see his son much more frequently. Now he's back to his old self – he's gone from strength to strength.

With the job of running a parish and trying to pretend to everyone that I could cope, and the simultaneous worries of looking after my mum who was very poorly at the time, and Keith, I was almost at the end of my tether. I really didn't want to confide in anyone in the church at that time. Everyone has their own worries in life and they didn't need to hear mine. That's not what my role is about. People were supposed to come to me when they were in need of support. I chose to just wear a smile and make out everything was fine.

As for me, well, work could have its benefits. Weddings, I have to say, could be a merciful release on our difficult days, after all, they are such happy occasions. But, at every wedding – without exception – the crunch point for me was when the couple were exchanging their vows. To hear them saying 'for better, for worse, for richer for poorer, in sickness and in health, till death us do part' – every time at this point there was a part of me that repeated my own vows. I'd say to myself, 'this is where you are now lass'. It's such an easy thing to say when you're young and healthy, but, come the crunch, can you still do it, can you still love someone that much? But in a way, that's ridiculous. Love just keeps coming doesn't it?

# A POSSIBLE CAUSE?

Keith really loved his work, which is just as well as it took up a lot of his life. He was always interested in trying out new farming methods, such as new techniques and varieties of crop. However, the down side to this was that it brought him into contact with all sorts of sprays. In the early days, when Keith was attending college, they didn't wear the spray protection that is made available nowadays. When I first knew Keith I often saw him working on his tractor without wearing any protective clothing at all while he was spraying. 'Oh, it's okay,' he'd say, 'that one's not dangerous.'

Looking back though, I can't help thinking all those years of spraying chemicals on the land helped to exacerbate Keith's condition. Let's face it, the regulations covering spraying over the years have become tighter and tighter. Mostly these days farmers need to be totally covered from head to toe before they are allowed to spray pesticides and such like. But what about those early years? What was going into Keith's system?

I can remember Keith using a spray which was used to protect crops from Codling Moth. Basically, these moths lay their larvae on apples and damage the fruit.

Even though Keith wore protective clothes when using this particular spray, I could even taste it in the air when he came back to the house in the evening. It was on his clothes and I'm sure it must have got into his system. You can't fully control where a spray goes, however careful you are. Sometimes I'd tell Keith that the conditions would be ideal to spray but he always tended to be a little more cautious, particularly if he felt the direction of the wind could send the spray towards residential areas nearby.

Surely, if a spray kills off bugs by getting into their systems, it could also affect the people responsible for spraying it? Keith had quite a sensitive skin and, sometimes, after spraying, he would come out in a rash. I'm no expert in this area but I'm pretty sure in my mind that there has to be a connection. A lot of the basic contents of many sprays have not changed over the years and this begs the question that, if they've had to tighten up the regulations regarding protective clothing when using these sprays, why wasn't it deemed necessary all those years ago? It seems people just didn't realise the damage that could be done.

Yet Andrew clearly remembers that Keith would not allow any of the boys to get near to the sprays he used when he was spraying the apple trees. Nor would he allow the boys any physical contact with him if he'd just had contact with any chemicals. 'It was a really acrid smell,' recalls Andrew, 'and Dad wouldn't even let us taste any of the apples after they'd been sprayed because it was important they were all properly washed prior to eating them.'

In November 2008, a 35-year-old environmental campaigner achieved something many others had failed to do when she was awarded a judicial review after a High Court judge ruled that the Government had failed to comply with its obligations under a European directive to protect rural residents from possible harmful exposure to toxic chemicals utilised during crop spraying.

The ruling came after a seven-year battle by Georgina Downs who began to suffer ill health at the age of 11. Miss Downs had experienced flu-like symptoms, a sore throat, blistering and other problems since being exposed to pesticide spraying while living at her parent's home which was situated adjacent to fields in Chichester, West Sussex. Miss Downs had gathered testimony from rural residents who had reported problems such as Parkinson's Disease, asthma and cancer.

The residents attributed their ailments to crop spraying in the vicinity of their homes. They claimed they had not been given any notification of the commencement of the spraying, while Miss Downs claimed that 'the government had failed to cater for the needs of residents who were repeatedly exposed to mixtures of pesticides and other chemicals throughout every year and, in many cases, like mine, for decades'.

In a landmark ruling the judge, Mr Justice Collins, agreed with Miss Downs and granted her a judicial review of the policy on pesticide safety and use. He added that Miss Downs had produced 'solid evidence' that residents in the vicinity had suffered harm and ruled that the then Environment Secretary, Hilary Benn, should rethink the way spraying was controlled and that the risks to human health should be assessed.

Defects in the Department for Environment, Food and Rural Affairs' approach to pesticide safety, he concluded, 'contravene the requirement' of a 1991 EC directive that harmonises the regulation of 'plant protection products'. Of course, after such a long-fought legal process, Miss Downs was delighted with the judge's decision, claiming that the crop spraying controversy was 'one of the biggest public health scandals of our time'.

One of Keith's colleagues at the agricultural college died a few years ago. He had Parkinson's Disease and I can't help wondering if his illness was caused by some kind of spray they used back in the early days. In the college they would spend a lot of time spraying plants in greenhouses – there was just no escape from it. If you just water your plants, some of that water goes on you. It's the same with sprays. Do you ingest it? These are just some of the questions that went round and round in our minds as we looked for the causes of Keith's illness – but then again, there are many other people who have Diffuse Lewy Body Disease who have never had anything to do with crop sprays.

Whether or not this horrible disease could ever be cured or attributed to crop sprays is obviously debatable but I found it interesting to hear Giles' viewpoint on both matters: 'On the whole, the best I could normally expect to do is to alleviate a person's symptoms rather than actually cure them,' he said.

'I notice that journalists in particular often write about 'cures' – they seem to like the idea that cures can be found for various ailments but, actually, if you get picky about cures – as I am – you'll find that there's very little that doctors can actually cure – we tend to manage, control and follow up – that's usually the way forward.

'If you look back through the 20th Century some diseases have become less frequent – TB is a good example – but the decrease has nothing to do with medications, it's attributed to better housing and sanitation.

'Could Diffuse Lewy Body Disease ever truly be cured? At this point I have to argue against my profession – let's not get sick in the first place. For instance, what's the cure for lung cancer? – *DON'T SMOKE!*

'There must be a reason why people get Diffuse Lewy Body Disease. We don't know what it is but it's reasonable to assume it's because of some form of toxin. The patterns for Parkinson's Disease around the world suggest it may be caused by exposure to some agro-chemical or petro-chemical.

'People have different tolerances. For instance, some people could lie out in the sun longer than others if they are already darker skinned. Such people would tolerate sunlight without such a high risk of melanoma as those with lighter skin. It may be that some people are more sensitive to chemical toxins than others.

'I suspect what will happen one day is that Parkinson's Disease and Diffuse Lewy Body Disease will just go away. It could be that those with responsibility for Health & Safety will take away whatever the chemical is that could be causing the disease. Remove the cause, remove the disease.

'I base this theory on an example of an outbreak of a particularly nasty illness on the Pacific island of Guam during the Second World War after the Americans had arrived. Basically, the illness was a combination of symptoms attributed to Parkinson's Disease and Motor Neurone Disease. When the war was over, medics took the opportunity to return to the island to investigate the cause of the illness. It was felt that if they could establish what had caused the outbreak locally it might help them to work out what causes Parkinson's Disease.

'What actually happened was, when the Americans returned to the island, the illness simply disappeared. One theory is that, when the Americans first arrived on the island they brought with them all sorts of foodstuffs not normally found on the island such as chocolate and hamburgers, and goodness knows what else they had introduced, foodstuffs alien to the local diet which may possibly have caused the outbreak.'

Could Parkinson's Disease or Diffuse Lewy Body Disease be hereditary? Giles has his own views on that too: 'If my father had something really dreadful, let's say Huntingdon's disease, I could have a genetic test which would prove or disprove whether or not I had inherited it. If that test proved positive what would I do? Basically, there would be nothing I *could* do about it so what would be the point of knowing?'

So, as you can see, it could be some time before we get definitive answers to our questions. Quite simply, there is still much to learn about Diffuse Lewy Body Disease. Diagnosis is also tricky – even for the experts – as Giles explains:

'Diffuse Lewy Body Disease is sometimes described as the 'second most common form of dementia'. Many of those in the medical profession who are writing stuff about their particular field of expertise will find a way of putting together data that makes their illness most prevalent. Those researching multiple sclerosis often describe it as 'the commonest cause of disability in young adults'. I am the medical director of a migraine clinic in London so maybe I could also claim that migraine is one of the most likely causes of disability!

'Dementia is really a pattern of symptoms rather than a diagnosis and, regrettably, it is sometimes diagnosed as Alzheimer's. A common cause is hardening of the arteries – vascular dementia – which is practically impossible to distinguish from Alzheimer's.

'Diseases of the brain can be difficult to diagnose accurately. In the mid-1980s a neurologist went to a brain bank to study 100 brains of people who had been diagnosed in life with Parkinson's Disease. Of the 100 brains he examined he concluded that only 75 of the deceased actually had the disease at all. As a consequence of this specialist's autopsy study neurologists have changed the definition of what they call Parkinson's Disease.

'Basically, Keith's nerve cells were dying and we don't yet know how to replace, repair or protect nerve cells in the brain because the brain is so complex, and that means we are not able to address the underlying cause of the illness – that's our holy grail in neurology, establishing how to deal with premature cell death.

'What we can do, however, is replace the nerve chemicals that the dead cells formerly made. It's rather like when a lady gets to 50 and loses her periods – you can't fix the ovaries but you can replace the chemical they produced. That's how our treatment works. We need to get in early.

'In the case of Parkinson's-related diseases we do need to wait for the symptoms to be bad enough before patients will get a great response to treatment. The difficulty with someone like Keith was should I have gone in earlier with the Exelon? Maybe I should. On the other hand, if I had, would we have noticed the benefit?'

# KEITH – IN HIS OWN WORDS

The very first session in the writing of this book took place in 2008. I was keen to get a first hand account of Keith's thoughts about the way this cruel Diffuse Lewy Bodies Disease has affected his life so I invited my co-author Ivan to visit Keith and me at The Rectory so he could talk with Keith.

Time was of the essence. It is not uncommon for sufferers to completely lose the ability to speak and Keith was no exception. By now his voice was almost completely inaudible and I knew if we waited much longer this would be an opportunity missed.

What follows is a three-way conversation between Keith, Ivan and me. You will notice that after each question, the actual time taken before a response from Keith is logged. Our questions and prompts to Keith are in *italics*, his responses are in **bold** type. If you count slowly in your head where the times are shown, you will have a reasonable idea of how the conversation progressed.

*Ivan: Keith, how old are you now?*

11 seconds

Keith tries to speak but it's practically inaudible.

*Pat: You're 74. You were born in 1934.*

*Ivan: Can you remember how long you've been married?*

4 seconds

**F . . . forgotten**.

*Pat: We've been married 38 years. We married in 1970. Is that right?*

3 seconds

**Yes.**

*__Ivan:__ I understand you have good days and bad days. How would you describe today?*

11 seconds

*__Pat:__ Is it a good day today, darling or a bad day?*

10 seconds

*__Pat:__ It's quite a good day isn't it?*

7 seconds

**Yes.**

*__Ivan:__ If you have a bad day Keith, how is it different?*

5 seconds

*__Pat:__ Can you answer that question? How does it feel to have a bad day, do you feel more wobbly or confused?*

10 seconds

**Wob . . .**

*__Pat:__ You feel a bit wobbly?*

3 seconds

**Yes.**

**_Ivan:_** _Does this disease make you feel tired?_

3 seconds

**Yes.**

**_Ivan:_** _All the time, or a lot of the time?_

Keith looks around the room, his eyes barely focusing on anyone.

18 seconds

**It's . . .**

4 seconds,

**. . . effort.**

11 seconds

**Wake . . .**

7 seconds

**. . . quarter past . . .**

5 seconds

**. . . 10.**

**_Pat:_** _Then by quarter past 12 you're fast asleep again!_

5 seconds

**Yes.**

*Ivan:* Are you angry Keith or bitter that you feel this way or do you just accept it?

10 seconds

*Pat:* Keith? Let's just try one question at a time. Are you angry about the disease?

4 seconds

**No.**

5 seconds

**Don't think so.**

*Pat:* Do you just accept that it's there?

7 seconds

**Yes.**

*Ivan:* Do you resent it, the fact that it's stopped you doing things?

8 seconds

**No.**

*Ivan:* So you don't get angry, you just accept it?

4 seconds

**Yes.**

*Ivan:* What do you miss being able to do?

After 15 seconds, the question is repeated.

12 seconds

Keith's eyes close, so his arm is rubbed to stir him.

***Pat:*** *Shall I give you a series of things and you can just say yes or no?*

Keith nods instantly.

***Pat:*** *Do you miss driving?*

Keith nods.

***Pat:*** *Do you miss gardening?*

12 seconds

**Stopped me . . . gardening.**

***Ivan:*** *Did you have hobbies before this illness, Keith?*

12 seconds

***Pat:*** *When you were younger Keith you enjoyed lots of sports, didn't you?*

A broad smile immediately appears on Keith's face as fond memories of playing county level hockey are stirred.

***Pat:*** *Did you play hockey for Suffolk and Essex?*

5 seconds

**Yes** (albeit rather confusedly).

***Ivan:*** *Do you find your illness frustrating?*

17 seconds, Keith mouths something but it's inaudible.

***Pat:*** *Do you miss going out for a lovely meal and things like that?*

Immediate response: **Yes**.

***Pat:*** *And you used to love our holidays abroad, do you miss that?*

10 seconds

**Yes**.

***Pat:*** *It's amazing, having lost the ability to do so many things, Keith very rarely shows any signs of frustration. He's an incredibly patient man, he always has been. If it was me, I'd be crawling up the walls. I guess being married to me he's always had to be patient! When you think that Keith used to have an incredibly large orchard which he had to prune on his own, he would just patiently work his way through it. It never worried him. I suppose when you grow things you can't be any other way than patient.*

***Ivan:*** *Did you know anything about this illness before you had it?*

15 seconds, no answer.

***Ivan:*** *When did you first notice that things weren't quite right? What did you notice first of all?*

20 seconds pass as Keith tries to answer. There's a few inaudible words then we hear:

**Couldn't believe it.**

**Pat:** *Can you remember Keith, all your right side swelled up, didn't it? Your right hand, your right leg and your right foot. I used to massage it to try to keep the swelling down and the doctor thought you might have gout or arthritis. Can you remember that?*

5 seconds

Keith nods.

**Pat:** *And then we went for a check up. Can you remember, you made me go too because I had a heart problem? That's when your illness was first identified.*

5 seconds

Keith nods.

**Ivan:** *Was it a shock when you were told or was it a diagnosis you didn't recognise?*

No answer, Keith just looks a little confused.

**Pat:** *Can you remember, the doctor telling me while we were on holiday that he thought you might have Parkinson's Disease? Then I had to tell you. Keith wasn't feeling too well and I noticed he wasn't moving as fast as he might. He was always fairly nippy. In fact, when he played hockey he was like a little terrier.*
*We've got pictures of Keith playing hockey with his head down and charging around. But several times during that holiday while in the kitchen I'd turn around and nearly burn Keith because he'd be standing so closely behind me that the saucepan would almost touch him. He'd lost his spatial awareness. Then he'd experience terrible nightmares. He'd jump all night . . . it was all to do with the same thing, but we didn't realise it at the time. Do you remember all that Keith? It was before you retired but it's a long way back now isn't it?*

114

Keith nods.

*__Pat:__ I remember the diagnosis clearly. Poor Keith, he just went into his shell.*

*__Ivan:__ What is the worst aspect of this illness to you, Keith?*

24 seconds

**Memory . . . loss memory. . .**

Keith continues to try to speak.

25 seconds

**Confused . . . memory.**

*__Pat:__ Often Keith will start a sentence then not remember what he's trying to say. He's trying to find the words to continue but then forgets where he started. It must be very frustrating for him, but he doesn't show it. It's very isolating.*

*__Ivan:__ What gives you pleasure these days Keith?*

Over the next 35 seconds Keith struggles to say something but without success.

*__Pat:__ Keith's still got a great sense of humour. If his carer Teresa and I are laughing or joking about something, Keith loves to laugh with us. Sometimes we just get into some really silly situations and it gets to a point where you either have to laugh or cry. Once that makes Keith laugh, we all start laughing. What about when the family and the babies come? That makes you smile doesn't it?*

Keith smiles instantly.
*__Pat:__ And when I kiss you goodnight?*

A broad grin appears on Keith's face.

5 seconds

**Yes**.

*__Pat:__ Keith did say in one of his really articulate moments that he loves it when I've been out and that the first thing I always do when I come in is to give him a kiss. He told me 'I love it when you come and greet me as you get home'. With my ministry I'm often out of the house. We used to laugh because most men would say to their wives 'what are we having for dinner tonight?', whereas Keith would ask, '__are__ we having dinner tonight?'*

*__Ivan:__ Do you get bored, Keith?*

14 seconds

**Yes**.

*__Ivan:__ Very often?*

No answer. Keith begins to look very drowsy and he's struggling to keep his eyes open.

*__Pat:__ It must be __so__ frustrating for you Keith because you know exactly what we're saying but you can't articulate the answer can you?*

5 seconds

**No**.

*__Pat:__ Sometimes his words can be absolutely clear, but what Keith's saying in his head isn't quite what comes out. I find that frustrating too, especially when I have to say to him that I'm sorry I don't know what he's talking about. Then he'll try to start again.*

Keith appears to perk up and is more focused on the conversation going on around him.

*Ivan:* *How does it feel to have carers here to help you get washed or to get you to the toilet?*

20 seconds

**Don't mind . . . put up . . . with it.**

*Pat jokingly:* *His carers are very good, but he's had a couple when he'd have liked to have wrung their necks, haven't you?*

Almost instantly, and with a smile:

**Oh yes!**

*Pat:* *We've been so lucky, the vast majority of the carers we've had in have been absolutely lovely. Most of them spoil him rotten. They love him.*

*Ivan:* *Do you feel you have lost any of your dignity?*

15 seconds

**No.**

*Pat:* *That's probably because our carers have been so good. They always ask Keith if he would like to choose his clothes and would he like them to do this or that. They never just assume anything. It's me who's the bossy one . . . I tell him what he's going to wear some days!*

**Ivan:** *Are you reassured that your relationship with Pat is so strong?*

Keith nods.

*Pat:* Do you ever worry I won't be there?

5 seconds

**Yes**.

*Pat:* When we've talked in the past it's been one of Keith's big worries that the day will come when I can't cope with him. Sometimes when I'm tired and grouchy he must think I can't cope, but I will. Sometimes if I have time away he thinks I'm not coping but it's just because I need a short rest. Keith does worry a little bit about that. I suppose when you're so dependent on somebody it must be easy to feel like that. I'm lucky though, we've got our boys as well.

*Ivan:* Do you still enjoy your food, do you still have a good appetite?

5 seconds

**Yes**.

*Pat:* Keith can still eat well, although there are times when swallowing is difficult for him. Fortunately, we're out of that phase at the moment. There was a time when he just couldn't swallow meat, even though he could chew it. Good food, and wine, is still a pleasure for Keith. He still likes to go out for a drive, although nowadays, he can't walk very far. He likes to walk around the garden. Any further than that he needs a wheelchair which he hates.

*Ivan:* Why do you hate your wheelchair?

7 seconds

**People look . . . at me.**

*Pat: Keith feels as if he's on show in a wheelchair, he's never liked the limelight. I tell him people wouldn't bat an eyelid but he just doesn't like it.*

*Ivan: Can you remember what you did yesterday and the day before or do you forget things quickly?*

8 seconds

**Often . . . for . . . forget.**

*Pat: Keith often remembers being back at Greshams, the family farm. He can better remember things further back. In his mind he's really there at Greshams. The other day he woke up and was telling me he had to sell some baths. I knew exactly what he meant, although I'm sure no-one else would have. I know we used to have some old metal baths on the farm which had to be got rid of, so I know where Keith would have taken them. Last night he was talking about 'the cardboards' and I know he was talking about the packing between the boxes of apples. That's going back nine years but for Keith, that's a present reality. It's like it's happening now.*

*Pat: Keith, is there anybody else in the room right now, besides you, me and Ivan?*

25 seconds while Keith looks around the room.

**No.**

*Pat: Quite often, as you talk to Keith, he'll appear to be looking right past you, over your shoulder, because he thinks he can see someone behind you.*

The preceding conversation should give you an insight as to how Keith was when we began to write this book. It was a world away from our previous life which was packed with so much hard work, fun and vitality. But whatever Diffuse Lewy Body Disease had taken away from us, it could not destroy our love for each other. If anything, it brought us closer together than ever.

Ultimately, this was a battle we shared to the very end.

# HELP IS OUT THERE

We were lucky, we had carers and family support and I know that not everyone is so fortunate. I feel for those having to cope with looking after someone on their own. It just shouldn't be that way. I had to think for both of us at the same time. I had to remember what Keith's needs were and how they would be affected by anything else I had to do. If we were going out, had Keith been to the loo? Did his pad need changing? Had we got his tablets with us? Were we going somewhere where we could park easily? Did we need to take a wheelchair with us?

If we were at home, where was he? Was he downstairs? If he was upstairs, was he safe? What was he doing? Was he near anything sharp or hot or anything else he could hurt himself on? I couldn't rest for a minute, just in case something happened. I couldn't switch off. Even if I was in the house while the carers were there, I'd still keep a vigil on him.

Giles explained to me that very, very slowly, probably over a period of the next few months, Keith's medication would wear off again and he would deteriorate further and further. From our meetings with Giles I'd been aware that we would reach a point when Keith couldn't take any more of the medication, that there would be nothing else Giles could prescribe to arrest Keith's decline. I guess I was psychologically prepared for that.

I knew that at some point I wouldn't be able to change the balance of Keith's medication any more, and that had been my responsibility. Having lived with Keith, whenever I'd noticed fluctuations in his well-being, I'd contacted Giles and the balance of the medication had been adjusted accordingly. Giles would up one medication, maybe lower another to establish a balance that would most benefit Keith for the condition he was in at the time. I knew we were gradually going down a slippery slope and that we'd reach a point that whatever adjustments were made to Keith's medications there would be no obvious advantages.

Every time we made an adjustment it was a sombre feeling. That's when I realised we were just another step down the path leading to an

121

inevitable conclusion. But my main concern had to be Keith's quality of life at any given point. When Keith's condition improved after we changed his medication we knew he would eventually sink to an even lower point and, each time he picked up, it would not be to such a high point as before. My relationship with Keith changed completely. I was still his wife, but I was also his carer which meant we couldn't share any of life's problems such as financial worries, worries about our children or grandchildren.

-//-

Maybe you've just discovered someone you care about is going to need extra support. Maybe they are someone like Keith, or maybe someone who is handicapped or ill in some other way. Either way, it's a daunting prospect – and an expensive one! How on earth are you supposed to finance the care that's required? Who do you turn to? Basically, you've been thrown into the deep end of a swimming pool, you need to either swim or you'll sink straight away. Well, let me reassure you – there will be help out there somewhere in almost every aspect of care for almost every type of condition.

Let's look at Keith's type of illness. Locally, almost everywhere, there will be a Parkinson's social worker – your GP and Social Services should be able to put you in touch with them. In some cases there are even specialist Parkinson's nurses – Giles was the person who put us in touch with Keith's Parkinson's nurse – a lovely lady called Juliet – and it was she who ensured we had contact with a social worker who specialises in Parkinson's cases. This social worker had access to an enormous amount of information that turned out to be most beneficial to us in the times to come.

If you don't know where to start – ask your GP if a local Parkinson's nurse or social worker is available. In the event that this is not an option, you should go directly to Social Services to ask for help. There is a charter to which the Social Services must abide that they must help you to maintain *your* level of living while you are caring for another person. This is because it is still more economical to the state if a person is cared for in their own home rather than in a hospital or nursing home.

I want to make this clear: People live with Parkinson's Disease for 20 to 30 years. It is not a death sentence. Undoubtedly, it adversely affects the sufferer's quality of life but some people with Parkinson's Disease even run marathons or lead remarkable lives. I don't want anyone to pick up this book and think that because someone's been diagnosed with Parkinson's Disease that it's the end for them. Even with Keith, I knew it wouldn't necessarily be the Diffuse Lewy Body Disease that killed him, but probably something like pneumonia because that's what people who become immobile are most susceptible to, and that's a very gentle end.

People often think a diagnosis of Parkinson's Disease is the beginning of the end – and that's what Keith did. He withdrew socially, he wouldn't go out and do things, he wouldn't go out with his friends – not that there was any reason that he couldn't – he could still eat easily in public, but he did tend to stumble over his words and sentences a little bit. He was more clumsy but no amount of reassurance would persuade him that his world had not come to an end. Maybe we all secretly felt like that at the time. Now we know differently – you don't die *of* Parkinson's Disease, you die *with* it and that's quite different.

Since actually sitting down to write this book and actually pinpointing moments in time, it's been quite an eye-opener to see, laid out in print, Keith's journey from the original diagnosis right up to his death. It had been a real rollercoaster ride. Day by day we didn't tend to realise the rate of deterioration but, when it's been documented over a period of months or years, it's very striking. When I first began noticing Keith's symptoms, I'd thought how bad his health had become, little realising at that time, how much worse was to follow. Then, every time I thought things were pretty bad, that things were probably as difficult as they could be, that dreadful disease conspired to prove me wrong again and again. So then I knew – however bad things may have seemed at the time – however limited Keith's abilities may have been – there was worse, much worse to follow. It was inevitable.

I think I knew when we'd probably reached the end of the road as far as gaining marked benefits from reducing Keith's Sinemet intake.

The peaks of improvements apparent each time his medication was adjusted were considerably lower than they once were. I guess we should have been thankful that the drug combination prescribed by Giles had such a beneficial effect for so long – that it gave Keith and I the opportunity to share so many aspects of our lives over the past few years that, otherwise, would have passed us by. All the more reason then to appreciate the importance of the help we received from so many individuals along the way. We certainly could not have managed without them.

Sometimes, because of Keith's double incontinence, sorting him out often required two people – myself and a carer – so I didn't like to be out of the house for long in case of a problem. On the other hand, I was able to do more in my office during the daytime while Keith slept more heavily but I found myself at the point of almost continuous exhaustion trying to balance my work/life commitments.

Thank God for such wonderful carers. Whatever would we have done without them? We were blessed. Lorraine was our first 24-hour Christie's Carer in April 2007. She was brilliant from the start. By then Keith had become used to temporary carers popping in and out to help with his physical care. Lorraine was a bubbly 56-year-old Aussie who brought so much laughter and pleasure into our home. Basically, she was out to see the world, working her passage as she travelled. For someone who had never undertaken such work before, she managed wonderfully – Christie's had given her basic training – and I was happy to have her helping out knowing that I would be around to assist her whenever the need arose.

Prior to her arrival Keith and I were rather apprehensive, which is hardly surprising when a total stranger is about to move into your home. As Keith was more 'with it' at the time, the transition from having a part time carer to a full time carer was really easy. Keith obviously liked Lorraine from the outset and they got on just nicely. I was obviously very relieved. Lorraine liked to keep busy and was happy to take Keith out occasionally for short rides in the car. She was a very practical lady and if ever she found herself at a loose end, would most likely be found fiddling around in the garden – at one time I even found her outside with Keith painting our garden furniture with preservative. We enjoyed having her around and were rather sad to see her leave for a five week break.

We need not have been concerned because, little did we realise it at the time, the day her replacement, a certain Polish lady called Teresa Leskovitz (we actually called her St Teresa) turned up on our doorstep proved to be a significant milestone in our ability to continue to care for Keith at home. Again, Keith hit it off with his new, temporary carer very well and we were pleased to see that, although Lorraine and Teresa were as chalk and cheese, they both shared wonderful but very different senses of humour. After her break Lorraine returned to care for Keith but when the time came for her to return to Australia we were fortunate to have Teresa agreeing to move back in to care full time for him.

Keith's confusion saw me contained to the home much, much more. He became very insecure when I was not around and he would not be very co-operative when Teresa tried to help him to bed if my work meant I had to attend evening meetings. Basically, Keith didn't like to be in his bed if he realised I was not in the house.

After a while Teresa had a much-deserved and much-needed two-week break and, even in such a short period of time, she noticed a marked deterioration in Keith's mental and physical states when she returned to The Rectory. He would just follow Teresa downstairs again and wait for me to return before he could be persuaded to go upstairs again for bed. Once, when I was about to go out of the door to babysit our granddaughter Bella, Keith was glaring at me almost angrily.

'What's wrong, darling?' I asked.
He frowned.
'Are you angry?'
As clear as a bell he replied: 'Yes.'
'Is it because I'm going babysitting?'
'Yes . . . I wanted to talk to you.'
The words came out from his mouth so clearly.
'Okay, darling, come and sit down and tell me what you wanted to say.'

Keith then sat down and delivered his concerns which, basically, were a whole load of gibberish. I had no idea at all what he was talking about. Nothing made the slightest sense but, having said his piece, Keith calmed right down and was happy to see me off on my way. Basically, I think all he really wanted was to spend just a little more time with me, on his own, to talk to, and I think that was rather nice although his insecurities in this respect could prove awkward at times, especially when he didn't even want me to disappear into the loo without him!

Basically, caring for Keith was a non-stop task. Teresa lived with us 24/7 and took just two hours off a day. She too became very tired but she never complained and had formed a very close bond with Keith. Let's put it in print : Teresa was brilliant! She was one of the BIG highspots of our lives. She was fantastic! She moved in with us shortly after Lorraine left and became a valued member of the family. In fact, whenever we thought of a family event it would have been inconceivable not to have her included, that's how close we became. Whenever she was away I was much more stressed and I'm sure Keith absolutely loved her.

Over the period of Keith's illness he had 10 different carers. One of them was, shall we say, rather challenging, and two others Keith, in his confusion, found difficulty in relating to, but all the others were top notch and they would all have been welcome to come back at any time to see us. Usually Christie's Carers only work with clients on a two-week basis and, because most of them seem to be foreign nationals, they tend to stay in Britain for a while then return to their home countries.

That said, it was fascinating to have carers from different countries in our home. Bearing in mind Keith's and my fascination for travelling when he was well, and how we so loved to experience different cultures, in a way, having carers talking to us about their home lands and cultures rekindled our interest in the far-flung corners of the world. These conversations were most stimulating for Keith and did him the world of good, making his days far more interesting than they would otherwise have been. He would love to listen to their tales and, in return, would enjoy showing them his photo album of

Greshams Farm and various milestones in his life so they had an insight into his world before he was taken ill.

Having so many foreign carers has also led to some mildly amusing situations. Most of them spoke very good English but often there was confusion in the way they put over what they were trying to say, while the range of accents we heard in The Rectory over those year were wide and varied – and not always that easy to understand.

After we made the transition to longer term carers, we found both Teresa and Lorraine to be absolutely marvellous. Keith seemed to be particularly at ease with Teresa and she was so good at planning ahead for his daily needs which simplified his routine and made life more manageable. That's why, whenever she returned briefly to Poland to visit her own family, Keith often found it difficult to adapt to the temporary carer assigned to look after him.

Teresa was tuned in to the needs of the *whole* family – as you can imagine, a village rectory is a pretty hectic place at the best of times with the telephone constantly ringing and visitors calling several times each day for one reason or another. For that reason, Teresa thought ahead all of the time, she anticipated just about everything Keith needed before he even realised it himself. She'd have his breakfast ready before he woke up and she made great efforts to plan the most nourishing and varied midday meals for him. She'd decide what was the best way of doing a particular task with Keith before he took it on in order to make it as easy as possible for him.

In fact it was Teresa who found a marvellous way to help Keith when, in the evenings after taking his Sinemet and Exelon tablets, he would begin to shake uncontrollably while sleeping in his chair which, of course, was distressing for him and to us all. Teresa discovered that by making a simple adjustment to the height of Keith's chair and moving him slightly into a particular position, the shaking could be stopped completely. Furthermore, she was not embarrassed by anything that happened – she just coped with anything that came her way.

During the summer of 2008 the weather generally was pretty dire but, come the autumn, Teresa decided it was nice enough to take Keith for trips out in the car. Sometimes they would head for the nearby seaside town of Felixstowe where Teresa would pop Keith into his wheelchair and push him along the front to buy an ice cream. It was such a shame when he was no longer well enough to do that as I know those excursions were always an enjoyable experience for him.

Teresa has a great sense of humour – she's invariably cheerful – but, what I appreciated as much as anything was that there was someone in the house each day I could actually talk to about anything. There was someone there all the time to help me when it was time to make a decision. That's not to say we always agreed with each other, but with Keith unable to offer an input into some of the more challenging decisions, it was good to have another adult around to chew over the pros and cons.

Teresa and I tried to balance out the work involved in caring for Keith during the day as well as we could. By the evenings Teresa was usually very tired indeed so I was normally the one who helped him to get ready for bed so that Teresa could get some sleep. Also, I tried to ensure that should Keith need anything in the night, that Teresa would not be disturbed.

Then she'd be up bright and early to prepare Keith's breakfast and his medication for the day. Sometimes it seemed like a military routine. It certainly needed to be.

Teresa recalls: 'When Keith was confused, this was the most difficult aspect of looking after him but it happened not so often to be too difficult to cope with. Sometimes, when he woke up, he was at his most confused so getting him washed and dressed could take some time. Sometimes, in his confusion, he tried to co-operate but only made things more difficult.

'Sometimes, when he was only half dressed he tried to walk downstairs without wearing his pyjama trousers. What should I do? Should I stop him or allow him to continue half naked? The situation could sometimes be quite stressful because if I let him go downstairs like that, anyone visiting would have thought it was my fault. He tried to do this over the Christmas period when everyone downstairs was having a meal. I'd asked him to stay with me while I washed

Andrew helps his father in the church at Simon and
Michelle's wedding.

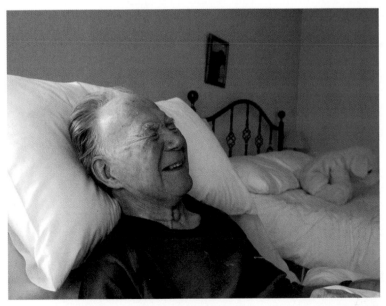

In spite of his health failing again, Keith still managed to keep
his sense of humour. He was never one to complain. Here, he
lies in bed in a fit of giggles.

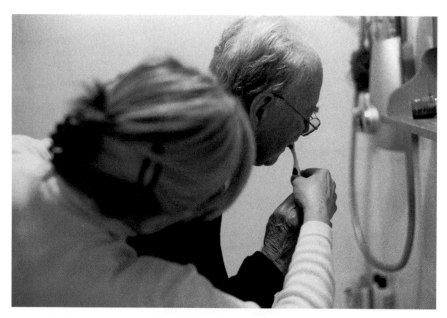

Keith's bedtime routine would take ages. Here, I'm, helping
him to clean his teeth.

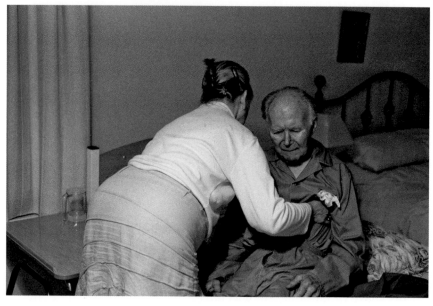

What seems like an age later, I manoeuvre Keith onto the bed.

In bed and comfortable at last. At this point Keith would often decide he wanted to talk to me!

Caring for Keith would frequently leave me feeling absolutely exhausted.

Ben shares a tender moment with his father.

Left: Keith is slowly
regaining
consciousness as I
hand over our new
grandson Noah for
him to cuddle.

A quite magical moment – Keith wakes up to discover he's holding baby Noah and, when we tried to take the baby back, Keith didn't want to let him go!

The last time Keith ever left home. Here his sister Pippa and Simon help him out of the front door. They were taking Keith to visit his mother's grave.

Left: It was important to keep family life as normal as possible. Here Kay and our little granddaughter Bella keep Keith company in The Rectory.

Carer Caz helps Keith take his medication.

Nearing the end, Keith drifts back into unconsciousness with baby Noah beside him.

A tender moment with my beloved husband.

Cheers Keith!

him but the next thing I knew he was making his way towards the stairs before I could stop him.

'You had to make yourself remember that Keith was a sick person as it could be frustrating trying to dress him when his body was not co-operating. He tried to help by holding on to things but that often just made it more difficult to dress him. In the early days I was wondering if he was working against me but now I realise he was only trying to help me. Sometimes when I tried to remove his trousers he would hold on to them. I realise now he was trying to remove them himself but was getting confused by pulling them up rather than pushing them down.

'People suffering from Keith's particular disease can sometimes become quite violent but you need to remember they are not being violent towards you, it is just a symptom of their illness.

'One day I had to struggle with him to persuade him to go into the shower. He was refusing because he had convinced himself there was a fire inside the shower compartment and he was too scared to go in there.

'I think Keith liked me. I really liked him and I believe we made a connection. It could be emotionally tiring for me when he was so confused. Every five to six weeks I'd take a short break, which I really needed. It was so difficult to look after someone like Keith. People who find themselves needing to care for a relative like Keith should not try to do it themselves. You must have help and you must realise that you need time for yourself too. You need to be able to recharge your batteries. Even on my daily breaks I liked to get out of the house completely, maybe to go for a walk in the countryside or go shopping. Time just for me, that was vital.

'I had several ideas of how to help to look after Keith. I often discussed these with Pat. Often she agreed, sometimes not but, at the end of the day, she knew what was best for Keith better than I did.'

Teresa often came up with good ideas and, like she says, we usually agreed on the best course of action to take. New faces bring new ideas. I compared it to cleaning the same room in the same way every time. You may find yourself missing cobwebs. If, however, you clean the room in reverse order, there's less likelihood of doing so. As for the violence she mentioned, Keith lashed out at me from time to time but only because he'd been confused and hadn't realised who I was. It was a defensive mechanism if he'd been frightened when I'd moved too quickly.

It was great to have long term carers – continuity in Keith's life was always the most beneficial. No matter how capable short term carers were, I felt Keith was having difficulty adapting to different routines and methods of care so I was very pleased that Christie's Care agreed to my request for carers to be provided over longer terms. There's no doubt in my mind that this was far better for Keith. We were so pleased that Teresa agreed to stay with us for the foreseeable future. It gave us a sense of security and well-being that was very much appreciated.

# THE IMPORTANCE OF FAMILY

Christmas 2008 was good. We had the family and Simon's in-laws staying with us over the festive period and, I'm pleased to say, we had a marvellous time and Keith really pulled out all the stops to play a part in the proceedings. Normally, Keith would not find it easy to have guests staying overnight because he found it so tiring. But, this time, he was brilliant. He managed to sit up until quite late and sit at the table for meals – and he even saw in the New Year! He even (in his way) managed to give me a kiss on the stroke of midnight. Looking back, I felt pretty certain Keith was actually enjoying this time – if he hadn't he would have just gone to sleep – so I'm sure the company we had was stimulating him. Keith was a stickler for tradition and would keep bottles of wines and port for a long time to open on special occasions. On this particular day Keith must have been feeling pretty good because Andrew recalls his father reminiscing of his schooldays and of the time he scored a try in a rugby match – a story that was indeed true, not one of those hallucinogenic episodes he'd experienced in the past.

How things changed. Just three months later we were down to very basic word skills. Maybe we'd get a yes or a no, a perhaps or a please or thank you, but that was about it. Sometimes Keith could manage complete sentences but they didn't make any sense at all. Over those months Keith had slowed down dramatically. He was becoming extremely confused again so we reduced his intake of Sinemet again to ease his confusion but, of course, this also served to slow him down physically. He became much more sleepy, sometimes not even coming downstairs each day until around 1pm. We had to change our bathroom around as Keith was no longer able to get into the bath. We installed a disabled shower facility which was rarely used until Keith fell twice in the bathroom. After these falls it was utilised every day.

It's dreadfully sad to see someone deteriorating before your eyes but, on one occasion, after I'd taken Keith upstairs to prepare for bed, I'd left him just for a short moment in the bathroom while he attempted to clean his teeth. I'd just made my way to the bedroom to fetch his pyjamas when I heard a thump. I hurried back into the bathroom to find Keith sitting crossways in the bath which, fortunately, was empty. His feet were in the air and his head against the wall. He had a very surprised look on his face and looked like a big banana.

Having ascertained he was totally uninjured, I found myself suddenly bursting out in laughter – he looked so funny sitting there like that. Keith just looked up at me and, within seconds, he too was laughing at his own predicament. It could have been a very nasty accident but at least on this occasion we could both see the absurdity of it all and share a moment of amusement – it's amazing that, despite everything Keith went through, he still managed to retain his sense of humour.

Keith began to fall over more often. He lost his sense of balance and often his feet became twisted around each other, particularly if he tried to turn around too quickly. Despite our best efforts it wasn't possible to watch him closely every second of the day but, thankfully, because he couldn't stop himself, he just gently fell and very rarely hurt himself.

We managed to acquire more devices to make life a little easier and more comfortable for him, including a head of the bed lift, and a special nylon sheet which enabled us to move him from one place to another. We had more handrails fitted in the shower room which were particularly helpful as Keith could no longer stand unaided long enough for us to dress him. The new handrails made this process a lot easier, and we also had a stairlift installed in The Rectory. Unfortunately, Keith became doubly incontinent which must have been particularly distressing and degrading for him, yet he seemed to just accept that this is an aspect of his life that just happened. He never, ever complained or got angry. In fact, whenever he had such an accident, he always seemed to be trying to help us as much as he could – even though his efforts rarely had the desired effect.

Following these deteriorations in Keith's health, our local GP visited regularly to keep a closer eye on him and to ensure we were getting all the support we really needed. From time to time, there was evidence of pressure sores beginning to form on Keith's bottom and, unless these were treated swiftly and appropriately, they could have become a source of considerable discomfort so it was always best to ensure they were not allowed to get out of control. Although, at times, there was not always a lot our GP could actually do, it was very comforting and reassuring to have him visit us on such a regular basis. Of course, not all of Keith's ailments were necessarily connected to Diffuse Lewy Body Disease so it was important that there was someone on hand who could recognise any other problems that may have been developing before they got out of hand.

Bearing in mind Keith's difficulties at meal times, family gatherings were more often hosted at The Rectory. Taking him to see our sons required such a lot of planning and we needed to take so much stuff with us to cater for his needs. At home, everything was at hand, all his home comforts were there, and there was less likelihood of him becoming too confused. I've already mentioned how Keith often found it difficult to swallow which is why we rarely ventured out for meals like we used too. However, on two occasions we made the decision to join family members for a meal and, somehow, not only did Keith manage to remain awake, he was able to have his meals without incident. There was, however, a price to pay – for the next few days he was knocked out.

The boys often joined us for meals at The Rectory. Most Sundays Simon and Michelle would turn up to join us for dinner. They would come over for the church service, then help out with the meal. We would often use these times to discuss how things were going with Keith.

Simon recalls: 'Mum would often ask Michelle and me if we had noticed this, or that. Living with Dad all week, any changes that had occurred would not have been so noticeable to her as they would to us having only seen Dad on a weekly basis. Dad was with us for many of these discussions but, sometimes we felt it would be better to chat away from him, depending upon what had been happening. Our visits really seemed to lift Dad – and Mum for that matter – but, if things hadn't been going too well, it wouldn't have made Dad feel any better if we had discussed the week's events in front of him.

'We always used to joke about Mum's cooking – particularly the quality of her Yorkshire puddings – we'd grade them from 0-10. It was always light-hearted banter, and Dad always tried to join in –

he'd done it all of our lives. But then it came to a stage when he couldn't even do that, and that was really sad.'

The highlight of my life while writing this book was seeing Keith attend Chelmsford Cathedral for the ceremony when I was made an honorary Canon which is, in layman's terms, the equivalent of the Church granting me an MBE for services rendered during my career. It didn't mean I had to do any extra work or that I would get any extra money, it was basically a 'thank you' from the Church in recognition for someone who has either been around for a long while or who has performed a particular task that has benefited the Church. I think, in my case, it was probably a bit of each. This was a huge honour for me and to have my friends and family there to witness this momentus occasion in my life in February 2009 was something I will never forget. Having Keith there too was just like having the icing on the cake. Prior to this occasion Keith had been quite poorly and I'd never have thought in a million years that he would have been able to come along.

I received a letter quite out of the blue from the bishop at the beginning of the previous December which told me of this prestigious honour. I was absolutely surprised and thrilled at the same time. The church secretary was with me when I opened the letter and noticed my face. 'Have you won the pools, Pat?' she asked. 'No, better than that, they want to make me a Canon!' Of course, I could hardly wait to tell my family the good news and, naturally, they were very pleased for me. I would love to say that Keith was thrilled for me too but, to be honest, it's difficult to say precisely whether or not he really understood what I was talking about when I shared my news with him. That said, I think he must have understood enough to make the superb effort he did to actually come along to the cathedral that Sunday evening.

I think he realised it was going to be a really special day for me. It was as if he made a special effort to conserve as much of his energy as he could the preceding couple of days but, even on the big day, it was by no means certain he would be able to come along at all. By this time Keith had really slowed up significantly and was spending the best part of the day sleeping. His medication had been adjusted to help compensate but without quite as much to benefit him as it had in previous months.

I conducted the normal Sunday services in the church in the morning and this was followed by a lovely family meal in The Rectory at midday. Keith joined us at the table though he struggled to stay awake for the duration. With the exception of my daughter-in-law who was away on a school trip, everyone was there which was absolutely lovely. By 4pm though I had to make my way to Chelmsford to prepare for the ceremony. As I left home Keith was deeply, deeply asleep. Teresa had been hoping Keith would be well enough to come to the ceremony but I told her not to worry. However, you can imagine my surprise and joy when, later that afternoon, I saw Andrew wheeling Keith in to the cathedral. One of my favourite photographs of this wonderful occasion is of the Bishop of Colchester, who is very tall, kneeling at Keith's feet so he could chat to him.

I remember as I and the other three recipients of this honour were walking down the aisle of the cathedral at the beginning of this ceremony, Keith's wheelchair was to one side of the aisle and I lightly stroked his shoulder as I passed him and made a supreme effort not to burst into tears. Better still, Keith actually managed to remain 'with it' all through the ceremony. Keith had always been there for me, through every milestone of my career – when I was made a reader, a deacon, a priest – so it was just perfect he was there when I was made a Canon. That said, the occasion totally drained him and, for the next two or three days, he was completely exhausted.

There's no doubt that Keith was at his happiest when the family come around. His face lit up when he saw our grandchildren, two-year-old Bella (Andrew and Kay's daughter) and 13-year-old Jonathon and our latest grandson Noah (Ben and Tonia's son). They were brilliant with him. A Bella visit was not an easy visit to sleep through – even Keith found that difficult, she's such a lively little girl. She'd chatter to her grandpa nineteen to the dozen. When she stayed overnight she liked to go to her grandpa's bed to help wake him in the mornings and to 'help' with his medication although, of course I should point out she was never allowed to actually get near any medicines.

She was so sweet and really loved Keith and loved to kiss him and could even understand that because of Keith's condition, he couldn't reciprocate. I remember the day we decided Keith would be well enough to hold her for the first time, and his gentle smile and joy on his face as he sat in his chair with Andrew and me either side of him for safety's sake as he cradled tiny Bella in his arms. What a memorable moment. At one time Kay and Andrew had been planning to move to Budapest in Hungary with Bella as Andrew had the opportunity to further his banking career out there. They had checked out the area and the office in Budapest and given the move some very serious consideration but, because of Keith's worsening condition, those plans were shelved as they wanted to be sure they could get back to us quickly in the event of an emergency and doubts about whether or not they wanted to raise their family in a foreign country.

For such a young man Jonathon was very clued up about his grandfather's condition. For the past few years he'd grown up seeing Keith in poor health and he probably couldn't remember him being any differently. He couldn't remember the days when he was small when Keith used to care for him or would pick him up from the day nursery. Yes, Keith spent a lot of his time looking after Jonathon but, towards the end, Jonathon was more than happy to repay him in kind. He always greeted Keith with a big hug and it seemed the whole place lit up when he arrived.

Keith's nightmares continued. We had an absolutely horrendous night while Teresa was away. I'd gone to bed very late and had disturbed Keith. He came out of his sleep, but not completely. His eyes were open but his nightmare continued. It was horrid for him, he was crying out like a really frightened child. He was pushing me away. 'Darling, it's alright, it's me,' I told him. 'No, no!' he was crying. This continued for some time, it was truly awful. Eventually I whispered gently, again and again in his ear 'I do love you darling' in the hope that when he reawoke the last thing he would remember was those words. I laid my head on his pillow next to his and, after a seemingly lengthy time, he began to settle and I became aware of his head being pushed up against my own as he snuggled up beside me.

Nursing Keith at home proved very expensive over the years and it was eating into our savings – but at least there is help available if you know how and where to look for it. That's something people really need to know more about. When I look back – this may sound very arrogant, although I don't mean it to – I'd anticipated what we needed and had that in place before Keith needed it so, before getting into desperation stage – although there were times when that occurred – on the whole I've been able to say I knew that such and such a service existed and that I was going to investigate it further. Often I did this before getting on to the authorities and told them that I knew this was possible, could they please organise it for us? That way, things often moved along more quickly than they might have otherwise done. It was much better this way than waiting until you're at your wit's end and having to wait for a doctor to write letters asking for help.

I also knew about another local charitable organisation known as Tendring Crossroads who, although they don't provide live-in care, will help out with housework and will sit with people in order for the live-in carer to have an opportunity to get out of the house for a while. This specialist organisation, which is registered with the National Care Standards Commission, is staffed by volunteers who will do whatever the regular care would normally do without significantly changing the patient's routine.

Crossroads offered 48 hours of free care while we were being assessed for the care Keith would need. In my case, that was like someone giving me gold! When you're _so_ tired, having been up all night and awake all day, they are a Godsend. I actually contacted them before Social Services suggested it, so they were already in place. I thought I knew about most of the schemes available to carers out there but I've since discovered there's a whole network of agencies in place that can help out.

Because earlier on I'd been caring for my mother towards the end of her life, I'd heard about Christie's Care, who Teresa works for and who provide 24-hour live-in care for all spectrums of society who may need them. They may be young and disabled, or older and needing a companion, or for people who for whatever reason are unable to get out and about. Basically, the carers come into your home, provide care and take over many of the chores and responsibilities. At first I cared for my mother myself but it was very reassuring to know there was an organisation such as Christie's that I could turn to later should I be finding it too difficult to cope.

Christie's fees vary, depending upon the level of care required. At one point that came to around £440 a week. Thankfully, there is some means-tested financial help from Social Services towards this. Basically, they look at any income against any expenditure such as electricity and water bills, rent or mortgage fees and so on, before coming up with a decision about how much you can get. At first they asked me if I had to do the washing for Keith every day. At that stage I wasn't, but once Keith became incontinent, his bedding and clothes needed to be washed every day which, obviously, added to the expense of caring for him, so that also had to be taken into account.

I know that some people like to keep their financial affairs private, they don't want others to know how much they have or have not got, but you do need to be totally open about your finances if you are to receive the support your require.

I know some would argue that, having paid their taxes, they are entitled to receive the financial support in any case, but it just doesn't seem to work that way. That means that *all* of Keith's pension had to go in the pot to pay for his care. Basically, if someone had to go into a nursing home to receive the care they required would cost somewhere in the region of £375 a week.

In fact, when Keith spent a week in a local care home to give me some time to recharge my batteries, his care cost £750 and that's a considerable sum for any family to find, particularly if the need for such care becomes more frequent.

# DEEPEST LOVE

Keith's illness changed me so much. It slowed me right down. It made me far more passionate about helping him. I was always the fussy one but Keith's illness gave me more of an insight into what other people have to cope with. I once went through a phase where I found it very difficult to make hospital visits as part of my ministry. I could still cope with taking funerals, but my emotions were harder to cope with. I had to recognise the fact that I was only human yet I felt a guilt that I was not in a position to do as much as I would have liked in the parish.

Not being able to communicate was also hard to bear and there were times when I'd have liked to share a spontaneous cuddle with Keith but he'd forgotten how to cuddle – although he showed me so much love in his own way. I missed the intimacy of our relationship. We slept apart because Keith moved around so much in the night. When Keith was having his nightmares and throwing himself around in the night, I was finding it difficult to function each day owing to the tiredness I was experiencing.

Even something as simple as sharing a cuddle required a little guidance. I'd tell Keith he should put one arm around me here, the other there and when to squeeze. That usually resulted in fits of the giggles between us. Keith would sometimes offer me a little, gentle kiss – I'd kiss him many, many times each day – but he could never come to me to give me a kiss or greet me at the door with a hug like he used to. Because of his condition, those moments were no longer possible. It was just something we had to learn to live with.

At the end of the day, I *knew* Keith loved me. Throughout his illness, his ability to show his emotions had gone up and down. At some stage he lost the ability to cry. I'd only seen him shed tears a couple of times since he was diagnosed, the first time was that first Christmas when he realised the gravity of his situation, the second time when our granddaughter Bella was born after a very worrying pregnancy, He could grieve, but not cry, there were no tears. He'd just go very, very quiet.

By 2006, it had got to a stage when Keith couldn't tell me he loved me, and this went on for a long time. He couldn't offer loving gestures, although he was still able to respond to them. Then came the time I went on a pilgrimage. I was in Assissi. This was a bad time for Keith. Somehow he'd got it into his mind that I'd left him for good. His brain just couldn't compute that I'd only gone for five days. I made a point of telephoning him regularly while I was away and then, suddenly and, in a very quiet voice, I heard him say 'I do love you, you know'. It may have been quiet, but it came over as clear as a bell and I came off the phone in floods of tears. I can't imagine what people near me must have thought when I apologised and cried out that my husband had just told me he loved me! What a wonderful moment, which was shared by my travelling companions, many of whom were also in tears!

Language fluctuation is one of the most difficult things to cope with as far as Diffuse Lewy Body Disease is concerned. The ability to speak varies so much. It comes and goes. Often we'd get to a stage when we thought Keith's ability to speak had gone completely and we began to live with it and then, suddenly, he was speaking again. I never knew each morning whether or not Keith was going to be able to speak to me. Some days, it was complete and utter gobbledygook, other days, he made perfect sense.

Keith usually couldn't even remember when it would be a good time to greet me with a hug – and that was something that would keep me going for the rest of the day when the emotional tank was running a bit dry. When I told Keith I loved him, sometimes, he could just about manage to say 'I love you too' which was such a joy that I kept telling him I loved him again and again just in the hope I'd hear him say it back to me! I was saving them up in the memory bank for the future!

By 2008 I think we were probably closer than we'd ever been in our lives. There was an intimacy that's not possible unless you've been through a situation like this. I was having to think for both of us and I had to try to get inside Keith's head to know what was the best way to help him and I just knew that he really appreciated what we all did for him – it's just that he couldn't articulate it.

Obviously I'd been forced to contemplate life without Keith. I guess in one sense I'd always done so because of the age gap between us. We had often discussed between us the possibility of me one day being on my own, not in any great depth, but it was a given likelihood that there would be a time when I would be left on my own if life took its normal path. The boys had also always been conscious of the fact that Keith was so much older than me and had often asked me how I would cope.

But the prospect didn't frighten me at all, I'd lived with it for too long. It saddened me, obviously, because everyone who gets married has visions of spending the rest of their lives together and of what they would do together in their retirement. I guess I'd just come to accept the fact that there was a far greater likelihood of me surviving Keith than the other way round. Also, I'd already done a lot of grieving for Keith, sometimes very, very deeply which, fortunately, most people were unaware of. I preferred to grieve alone by shutting myself in a room and immersing myself in writing music. There were times when I desperately needed my own space. I didn't go out for long walks though – I was more of a lazy griever!

Sometimes I found it nice to look back at old photographs of Keith and me – other times I found it quite a sobering experience. I think back to the time when Keith decided to help decorate our Christmas tree which was, shall we say, an interesting experience. We had what was basically a rather unstable tree being decorated by an even more unstable, confused husband trying to help me. Before long one branch had about six or more decorations on it while others had nothing at all. I remember him standing back to admire his handiwork and then looking as if something was not quite right but not realising quite what it was.

I rediscovered a video camera with footage of Keith on it. Bella could only have been around four months old at the time of the recording. As I'd been filming, Keith had wandered into the study and was looking directly at me. I explained that I was holding a video camera and perhaps he would like to do something for the camera? Keith responded by pulling a silly face and waggling his hands besides his ears. It was so funny and nice to see his humour resurfacing for such a brief moment in time and, watching it again on the video brought back some lovely memories of how he used to be. But I'm also reminded that, at the time, I'd been thinking Keith's condition was bad, but it was certainly nowhere near as bad as it became. Quite a sobering thought. Fortunately though, whenever I got bad days with really negative feelings – after all, Keith was only going to get worse – 'St Teresa' was usually on hand to buck me up again.

Keith liked continuity and he loved everywhere to be tidy. This often caused problems because he tended to find things lying around and would put them away in the most inappropriate places! In the past I'd found my tights in the bathroom cabinet and bottles of milk in the oven. Sometimes when I went into my office in the front of The Rectory I discovered papers were missing. When he was well, Keith hated paperwork so made sure everything was kept up to date in order to make the task as easy as possible. Unfortunately, his efforts tidying my office had the opposite effect! Yes, Teresa and I often found interesting things in interesting places.

I'm often reminded of the time Keith stayed for a couple of days and nights in a superb residential home, Blackbrook House, in nearby Dedham. Keith had a habit of removing his glasses and laying them down somewhere, as did many of the other residents. As a result, many people's glasses ended up on someone else's noses. Unfortunately, Keith's glasses were brand new and quite expensive but we were never able to find them again, even though one lady who was sitting near him had piles and piles of glasses in her cupboard drawers that didn't belong to her.

There was, intentionally, quite a lot of noise in Blackbrook House, designed to stimulate the residents. There was also one poor lady there who, obviously, fancied Keith! She had absolutely no idea I was Keith's wife. She'd keep sitting next to Keith and saying to me, 'He's a bit of alright, isn't he?' 'Oh yes,' I'd reply, 'he's pretty good.' 'Oh I *really* like him, is he free?' she'd ask. I explained that we were married, that I was his wife. 'Oh, we can soon sort that out,' she replied. She had no idea of what she was saying, poor thing. But Keith *did* have some idea – and he was looking at me in total panic! I

150

guess I should have been somewhat flattered that, even at his age, someone was still fancying my lovely husband.

Illnesses such as Keith's can raise all sorts of situations. When a person is unable to care for themselves it falls to others to do what they can to help them, including taking them to the toilet or to help wash them down. At first I felt very awkward about our boys being required to help Keith with such deeply personal requirements. Fortunately, they didn't feel awkward about it at all and each of them would not think twice about cleaning up their father after a visit to the toilet. What concerned them far more was that this frail old gentleman was their dad, a man who not so long ago was a fit and active person, reduced to a shell of what he was. The boys were just the same when they helped my own mother, their grandmother. At least that experience helped to prepare them for what was to follow with Keith.

Simon puts it into perspective: 'At the end of the day, Dad did all that for me when I was a baby and I think it would have been very difficult for Mum to cope with everything without 24/7 care. But I don't worry about things like that, I didn't have a problem with it.

'When the issue first arose, I was the only son available. I was living at home and out of work, while Ben and Andrew were both working away. Looking back, I was still being treated for my drugs problems. This was the flip-side of those problems. As a result I was available to help Mum and Dad and, in doing so, it was making me feel so much better. Caring for Dad was almost like my way of saying 'thank you' for all he'd done for me over the years. It was very therapeutic for me. I really felt I needed to pay Mum and Dad back for all the support they'd given me.

'Prior to the carers coming in to help Dad, I did as much as I could to help out as I was making my own recovery. I think Mum realised though that, if I was going to get back on my feet I needed to get a job of some kind and not just be at home to help care for Dad. That was when it was decided to find out about getting a live-in carer.'

Keith's illness didn't really affect my faith at all. I didn't get cross with God because I believed there was a cause for all this. I still believe the trigger was the stress Keith was under while I was working away from home so I must take some responsibility for it. It could have been so much worse. I knew so many people were praying for Keith and I'm sure that's what got us so far. Keith's faith certainly hadn't decreased, in fact, I'm sure it increased if anything. He was not well enough to get over to the church any more but, whenever I asked him if he'd like to receive communion at home, he always wanted to.

Keith's illness had been so gentle, and I knew there were so many people out there who were ready and willing to help us and that gave us so much strength to cope with the day-to-day trials we had to face. We all have to die, one way or another. It's my belief that something like this is caused by the sins of the world. Not Keith's sins, but we live in an imperfect world. We have imperfect relationships with people and God and between us and nature.

There are some things that I will never know the answer to. Given a choice it would be lovely to live in a perfect world but I didn't blame God for Keith's illness. I wasn't angry with God, and neither was Keith. I did get angry with what had happened but I didn't say 'why him?' or 'why us?', although I wish we hadn't had to go through all that. It's not something anyone would choose. God was in this. He hadn't deserted us – although there were times when it felt as if He had. I needed time to be alone with God but I didn't have that time as often as I would liked.

The love Keith and I had towards the end of his life was much deeper than it ever used to be because of what we were going through at the time. We have God to thank for that. I suppose we turned it around and were looking at things from a different perspective. One day, I thought, all this would eventually make sense. Despite all the odds, Keith was still with me and I'm convinced that, with similar packages of care and medication, there's no reason why the life expectancy of some other sufferers of Diffuse Lewy Body Disease could not be extended as had been the case with Keith.

Looking back over some of the letters exchanged between Giles and our local GP Dr Bettle, I am reminded of just how fortunate I was still to have Keith with me. On 27th July 2006, Giles had written:

152

*'(Keith) is in a palliative phase of the illness and the main treatment target is maintenance of cognition . . . he has a thoroughly unpleasant, progressive neuro-degenerative condition for which treatment is purely symptomatic. I am surprised he has lived this long and think this is because he is having excellent care at home'.*

In January 2007 Dr Bettle wrote: *'I think it is important to try and maintain him (Keith) at home rather than he be admitted into an institutional facility of some sort as he has moments of at least partial lucidity mixed in with periods of great confusion and hallucination. I think it would be to his disadvantage to be in unfamiliar surroundings and I am sure this would further worsen his confusion as he moves into the terminal phase of his illness. Unfortunately, I think it is very hard to guess how long his life expectancy is given that he has already surprised us'.*

Giles' letter, addressed to the City of London Medical Centre later that month informing them of Keith's condition, made depressing reading: *' . . . it is quite possible that his life expectancy is now three to six months, though this is impossible to predict with any accuracy'.*

Yet here we were in 2009 with Keith still confounding medical experts. Somehow he was still with us and still able to enjoy a reasonable quality of life. Life is so precious and, although the combination of medications prescribed to Keith had undoubtedly extended and improved the quality of his life, there are no guarantees it would do the same for everyone. But the experiences Keith and I shared over the past nine years convinced me that, surely, it's got to be worth trying.

I thanked God – and Giles – for helping Keith beat the odds. I knew there were no guarantees and that Keith's health was bound to deteriorate in the weeks and months to come. There was a certain inevitability of this.

A few months prior to Keith's death Giles wrote to me to say: *'I agree that Keith's survival is amazing and I think there can be no doubt that this is a consequence of the excellent care which you have provided'.* That may be true, but I couldn't have done this on my own, there were so many others who have played their parts in making Keith's life so much more bearable.

# A SCARE AND MAGICAL MOMENTS

It was back in 2006 that I felt a small lump on the side of my neck. I was worried it may have been cancerous so I hurried along to see my GP. 'No, no,' he reassured me, 'it's not cancer. I don't think it's anything serious at all, but to be on the safe side, we'll monitor it.' There was no noticeable difference in the lump afterwards, at least, not until just after Christmas 2008 when I noticed a certain amount of discomfort. After a while I thought the lump was beginning to feel a little bigger. It was when I was trying to go through the church doors with bags in each hand that I fell backwards and banged my head on a flagstone.

From that point on, I noticed the lump in my neck even more and, when Andrew agreed with me that it had become larger, I went back to see my GP who also confirmed the lump had grown. However, as he had no idea what it was, he referred me to another doctor in Colchester. The doctor ordered an MRI scan to find out what was going on. When the scan came back, nothing abnormal was shown. As a result, the doctor did not feel that there was anything to worry about but felt it may be a good idea to conduct another MRI scan in three months' time.

By the time of the next scan in May, I was convinced the lump in my neck was increasing in size by the minute. I was really worried. It was also becoming quite painful and beginning to have an effect on my hand. This time, the MRI scan, which was done on a Friday, was a completely different experience. By the following Monday, I received a call from a receptionist at the hospital to inform me that the consultant had just seen the results of my latest scan and these confirmed that the lump, whatever it was, had definitely grown enough to become visible on the scan – this had not been the case with the first scan.

The consultant felt that my case was outside his field of expertise so arrangements were made for me to see another consultant, a head and neck specialist. The receptionist told me that the consultant was currently on holiday but, as a result of my scan, he would be coming in the following day to see me. Would I be able to come in at 4 o'clock tomorrow? Well, let's face it, whatever I'd planned for the next day would have to wait in the light of what I'd just been told.

The next day found me in the consultant's room. He was an absolutely lovely man. 'Now then' he said, 'I'm a cancer specialist . . . but that doesn't necessarily mean that you have cancer.' A tumour was definitely the cause of the discomfort in my neck. He felt the lump with his hands. 'That's really unusual,' he said. 'I can't decide what it is. If it's okay with you, I'll try a needle biopsy.'

This proved to be a very painful and, ultimately fruitless, procedure. The consultant apologised and said he was not willing to proceed any further while in Colchester as there were insufficient facilities on site. He wanted me to visit a group of experts in a sarcoma clinic in nearby Chelmsford.

Again, he tried to reassure me that I probably hadn't got cancer, though the fact he wanted to send me to a sarcoma clinic hadn't exactly convinced me that I didn't have it!

After my visit to Chelmsford, the experts were far from sure I had cancer and, to be on the safe side, decided they didn't want to disturb the tumour as they were still not sure what type it was. They referred me to a sarcoma centre in University College Hospital in London. By now, the lump was becoming increasingly painful and worryingly for me, no-one seemed to have much idea what it was.

Mr Kalavrezos, the consultant at UCH, a very pleasant man, was also unable to shed any light on the type of tumour I had but suggested a further needle biopsy to try to see what they could draw out of the lump and a further MRI scan was arranged. The needle biopsy, again, proved unsuccessful and even more painful than the one I'd had a couple of months earlier.

Again and again I had to return to the hospital for further tests. I was told the consultants would not want to start an operation to remove the lump until they could be sure what it was in case of further complications that could allow any potentially cancerous cells to spread around my body. Still came the reassurances 'it may not be cancer, we just can't be sure'.

At this stage my hand was numb and yet another needle biopsy was arranged. This too, was painful – excruciatingly so – and

156

unsuccessful but, by now the consultant decided it was not prudent to wait any longer as the tumour was still increasing in size.

Back home, Keith was aware of what was going on regarding my health. Poor Keith, he was really worried about me. He was still able to utter a few words at this time. Each time I'd returned home from meetings with specialists I'd tried to reassure him that all would be okay and he'd heave a huge sigh of relief, sometimes managing to say something like 'oh, good'.

With everything going on Teresa's workload inevitably increased. Obviously she also needed breaks but finding someone who could take over from her when she was away would not necessarily be an easy task. Sure, there are plenty of other carers out there but, for someone like Keith, continuity at this time was most important and finding someone that Keith could get on with, feel comfortable with, was vital. Fortunately, Christie's Care had another wonderful lady on their books, Carolyn Minto (or Caz as we called her) and, almost immediately, Keith and Kaz forged an excellent relationship which was a huge relief, I can tell you!

Teresa and Caz were very good, constantly reassuring Keith whenever I had hospital appointments, but he was still concerned, I'd say probably as much as he would have been had he been healthy at the time. I have to admit, I was more than a little concerned for my own welfare at this time which probably distracted me to some degree from caring for Keith as much as I'd been able to prior to my own illness. Nevertheless, I still did as much as I possibly could, ably supported by Caz, Teresa and the boys who also did as much as they could to look after me as well.

Not knowing whether I had cancer or not was hugely worrying. My prayer at the time was, if I had cancer, please Lord, take Keith before me. He was deteriorating fast, losing weight, he was becoming less and less mobile, his swallowing was becoming even more laboured to the point he was eating mostly mushy food or soups, he was speaking fewer words, and sleeping more and more and, since Christmas, he would often spend the whole day in bed. If I died, where would he go? What would happen to him? If I wasn't around, he would not have been able to stay living in The Rectory – that came with my job. It was very obvious by now that time was running out for Keith and, I'd assumed, he could not last much longer.

If I was anxious, it was just as bad for the boys. Ben tells me that he was more worried about me at the time than he was for Keith. He'd already been preparing himself for the moment when he'd be losing his father, now he was thinking he'd be losing me first. Every time I went to the hospital for a test he was thinking, 'please let it be okay'.

In July, I was admitted into the hospital for my operation. Being a former nurse, I was somewhat reassured to find my bed was at the far end of the ward, some distance from the nurses' station. That meant they weren't too worried about me after all. The nursing sister came to speak to me as I sat, rather calmly as it happened, on the side of my bed. 'Now then,' she said, 'I don't want to worry you, but this is going to be a rather major operation,' and she began to explain what the operation would entail. Up to this point, I'd assumed I'd have a small scar, maybe a couple of inches long, on the side of my neck. I was in for a big surprise!

Then, a few moments later, the houseman came to see me. 'Now, I don't want to worry you but this is going to be a rather bigger operation than you seem to be expecting. When you come round after the op you'll have tubes coming out of here, and there, and there.'

'Okay,' I replied somewhat nervously.

Mr Kalavrezos came to see me next. 'This is going to be a much bigger operation than you think Pat. Just to be sure, we're going to move you up to the bed alongside the nurses' station.' The nurse then took my blood pressure which, not unsurprisingly, was sky high! My biggest fear was, that if it was sarcoma, that would be bad, bad news because sarcoma has a habit of travelling to the lungs and is not easily treatable. If anything happens to me, what will happen to Keith?

After the operation, in which the lump was removed, Mr Kalavrezos stood at the end of my bed when I came around. 'Was it cancerous?' I asked. 'To be honest with you, I still really don't know,' he said. For the next two weeks I was waiting for results to see whether or not I had cancer. It turned out my tumour was indeed on the cancer spectrum but I did not have sarcoma. That was a huge relief but, nevertheless, I then had to face a rather gruelling six-week course of radiotherapy – my tumour was benign, but aggressive, which means it would not throw off cancerous cells thoughout my body – I wouldn't get secondaries – but without the radiotherapy there would have been an 85 per cent chance it would come back and be even more aggressive.

So, every weekday for six weeks, I had to travel to London for my course of radiotherapy – time I had to spend away from Keith with, at the time, just Teresa at home caring for him. The sessions were very tiring, as was the travelling but, once home, I was needed to help look after Keith and, by the time I flopped into bed, I was completely exhausted.

It was not until November that I was able to return to work – six weeks after the end of my course of radiotherapy. Christmas capped off a very difficult year for the whole family, what with Keith's illness and mine, Ben's wife Tonia had given birth to our latest grandson Noah eight weeks early at the beginning of December which, obviously, proved very worrying too. In spite of Keith's failing health, he was aware of Noah's birth. We had planned a big family Christmas to coincide with my 60$^{th}$ birthday but, as Noah didn't come out of hospital until the week beforehand, Tonia could not come along. Otherwise, the rest of the family, including Ben, arrived and Keith had to make do with seeing photos of little Noah on the laptop computer.

On Christmas Day, Keith came downstairs and sat at the dinner table with the family although he could hardly keep his eyes open. We had hoped to take a family photograph but poor Keith could not stay awake. We tried the next day but, in the end, we had to make do with a group shot with the family around Keith who still was unable to open his eyes.

The following month, Keith and I celebrated our 40$^{th}$ wedding anniversary. Who would have believed we could possibly have reached this milestone when Keith was first diagnosed? Every year Keith and I had celebrated our anniversary by renewing our marriage vows. Over recent years though, Keith had been unable to actually repeat his vows so the boys and I would help him do so by saying his vows on his behalf and Keith would nod his head or say yes at the appropriate moment.

Of course, by the time our 40th anniversary actually arrived, Keith was completely unable to respond accordingly. We'd all gathered together for lunch, the boys, and Simon's in-laws too. The idea was that we would all renew our vows together and to mark this by lighting candles. It was decided that all the boys would help Keith renew his promise, then all the girls would renew theirs.

Years earlier, at a wedding ceremony, I'd heard a beautiful poem, called *I Will Be Here* by Steven Curtis Chapman. I loved this poem so much I'd pinned a copy of it up in my study. Every year from then on, I would read the poem to Keith on our wedding anniversary because it felt so appropriate to us as a couple and, here, I'd like to share it with you.

## I Will Be Here (Steven Curtis Chapman)

*Tomorrow morning if you wake up*
*and the sun does not appear*
*I will be here*
*If in the dark, we lose sight of love*
*Hold my hand, and have no fear*
*'Cause I will be here*

*I will be here*
*When you feel like being quiet*
*When you need to speak your mind*
*I will listen*
*and I will be here*
*When the laughter turns to crying*
*Through the winning, losing and trying*
*We'll be together*
*I will be here*

*Tomorrow morning, if you wake up*

160

*and the future is unclear*
*I will be here*
*Just as sure as seasons were made for change*
*Our lifetimes were made for these years*
*So I will be here*

*I will be here*
*and you can cry on my shoulder*
*When the mirror tells us we're older*
*I will hold you*
*and I will be here*
*To watch you grow in beauty*
*and tell you all the things you are to me*
*I will be here*

*I will be true to the promise I have made*
*To you and to the One who gave you to me*

*Tomorrow morning, if you wake up*
*and the sun does not appear*
*I will be here*
*Oh I will be here.*

It was not until early 2010 that our grandson Noah was well enough to be brought over to The Rectory to meet Keith for the first time. This was a lovely, lovely moment and one which Ben remembers with great fondness: 'I have a wonderful mental picture of that moment in my mind. Tonia and I handed Noah over to Dad while Mum hovered anxiously next to Dad just in case he dropped him. At this point Dad could no longer express himself and it was hard to know what he was thinking. With Noah in his arms he just beamed. It was a wonderful moment.

'After a few moments I think Mum was worried that Dad had had enough and she moved over to lift Noah from Dad's arms at which he immediately made a point of wrapping his arms around Noah even more closely than before as if to say 'you're not going to take this baby away from me!' For us all it was an absolutely incredible and memorable moment.'

There's no doubt in my mind that Keith knew exactly who Noah was but, when Ben, Tonia and Noah returned the following Palm Sunday, although Keith was still aware who Noah was, by this stage of his illness, he was unable to hold him. The following week, they returned. Keith was in bed but, in the space of seven days, he did not know who Noah was – nor for that matter, who Ben and Tonia were. That must have been very painful for them. Ben believes that although Keith did not respond to Ben's name, he still knew he was his son, or at least, someone he felt he should still care about. But, somehow, Keith still knew who I was so I had to be thankful for that. By this time, I'd had time to reflect upon my career. Back in January, at a prayer vigil, I'd come to the conclusion that the parish had been limping along because I'd been ill for so long, and because of all the time I'd been unavailable because of Keith's illness. Keith was now needing me more and more to such a degree I could hardly venture outside The Rectory. His deteriorating condition was proving a tremendous strain on Kaz and Teresa that it was only right that I should be there as much as possible to share the load.

Within a short while of returning to work in the previous November I found myself being endlessly tired out, exhausted in fact. The situation wasn't fair for the parish, it wasn't fair for Keith, and it didn't feel fair to me either. Something had to give. During the prayer vigil I was looking for an answer. It came, the answer was that it was time to move on. I just felt I couldn't take the parish any further. It has so much potential but I felt it needed somebody else, somebody fresh to take it further. I decided to tell just two people, Keith, and one of my closest friends, Sue Jones the parish secretary. I didn't want anyone else to know my decision until I was absolutely sure I'd got everything clear in my head.

I have to be honest here. Once I'd made that decision it was as if a huge burden had been lifted from my shoulders. Although I was still working at the time, I remember people telling me I looked different, what's happened? I decided I would announce my retirement at a church meeting in April but, prior to the meeting, rumour got out that I might be on my way. I knew Sue wouldn't have breathed a word about my decision but I was mystified how the rumour originated.

Any Christian will appreciate that the Easter period is one of the busiest in the Christian calendar. 2010 was no exception. To say it was hectic would be an understatement. There was meeting after meeting almost every evening and, despite his frailty, Keith was aware of this, of that I'm sure. How do I know? I can't really say, except that we were so close. When I came home late and tired, he'd look at me so sympathetically. That was just his way. On top of this I was still having to travel regularly to London for further acupuncture to cope with the effects of other treatments I'd been undergoing and I was also fully involved in the production of a church group production of *Jesus Christ Superstar* which was extremely labour intensive.

Then came a week when Teresa was away on leave and the usual cover was unavailable, therefore we had a carer called Patricia who didn't know Keith at all – a lovely lady – but she just couldn't manage to cope with him. And so it was I had to do absolutely everything to care for Keith. Patricia was with me but was unable to assist to any great degree because Keith made it plain he didn't want her to because he didn't know her. I was bathing Keith, dressing him, feeding him, putting him to bed, helping him up and down the stairs, toileting him – what would I have done without that hoist? – there were just not enough hours in the day. But I wouldn't change that week for anything because I did absolutely everything for him. It was like Keith and I against the world!

When Teresa returned, she was shocked. 'Oh dear,' she said, 'how he's changed.' It was plain to see. Keith's whole being was changing. His muscle tone was changing, his face was changing. Teresa was so wonderful. She tried so hard to ensure Keith had at least a couple of hours downstairs each day – just to keep him socialising with other people. But, in the end, we had to ask ourselves – is this fair, is this fair to Keith? It could easily take more than an hour and a half to help him eat his breakfast because of the difficulties he was having swallowing. Giving him a sip of orange juice was a major task and we had to crush his tablets so he could take them. He was so far down the line with his illness. He was just disappearing from us. It was heartbreaking.

It's hard to describe how I felt. I was Keith's wife but, at the same time, it was as if I wasn't. I decided I needed to be able to do some things on my own. Just for me. A little 'me time' if you like. I'd almost forgotten what it was like to be me. I think maybe every carer may feel the same way at some stage. You either just totally submerge yourself in the other person's illness or you don't do anything else or go anywhere. To some extent, that's exactly what you *have* to do if you really want to keep that someone at home with you but, equally, I felt as if I was drowning. I couldn't do the rest of my job because I was losing me. Does that make sense? So, sometimes after my hospital treatment in London, if everything was in place back home to care for Keith, I would go to a West End show before returning home. Even then, this was not a good time for me. There were lots of tears - lots of grieving in a way that I could not have allowed myself to do back at home. I guess I was preparing myself to finally lose the man I loved so much.

*DIARY ENTRY 4am MONDAY 14<sup>th</sup> MARCH, 2010*

*It is in the dark, early hours of the morning that one's thoughts go racing. It is just over a year since Ivan and I sat together talking through the events of the last 11 years to record the story of Keith's condition and so much has changed in that time and yet, in so many ways, much appears to remain the same, at least to the watching eyes of the world, those who do not have to see, day in, day out, hour in, hour out, the minute changes and losses that eventually drive to take Keith slowly and inexorably from us.*

*'How is Keith today?' is a question, though so well meant, that I have come to dread, because I no longer know how to answer it. Surely by now folk must be getting 'sympathy fatigue'? They must surely be weary of me say things are 'Oh much the same' or 'not such a good day today' or 'he's a bit perkier, thank you'. I do wonder if anyone has any idea at all of what this stage of the illness is really like! Perhaps I will try to describe it, so that you, dear*

*readers, who have picked up this book because you do want to know, may get a glimpse beyond this closed door, a door not many come beyond now.*

*Perhaps that is where I should begin – behind the closed door, where few venture. I ask myself whether that is my choice, or the choice of others? Do I keep folk at a distance nowadays to shield them from the reality of the presence of Diffuse Lewy Body Disease at the heart of our family, or to protect Keith – and ourselves – to maintain his dignity and to keep in folk's minds the man who still resides inside, deep inside, a mind and body which is no longer in his control? I think it is, perhaps, a bit of both.*

*The closest family, our sons, their wives and children are still a vital part of all that happens. They visit when they can and Sunday lunch still sees at least one of them with the family joining us. They are good times for Keith. He makes a tremendous effort to sit up the table with us, often now in his wheelchair for extra support and, occasionally, some sort of normality kicks in for him and he is able to summon the wherewithal to pick up his own knife and fork and at least partially feed himself. The chatter and banter of the family bounces around the room and, although Keith's response is no more than a whispered yes or no, some of the time, at least, it would appear that he has some idea of the comments being bandied around. Rarely now, but nevertheless, still happening, he will come out with a whole series of words which, although apparently random and unrelated, are Keith's efforts to participate in the banter. We respond as appropriately as possible, and although we have no way of knowing if our response is any more relevant than what Keith is trying to say, seems to satisfy him.*

*Staying a little longer with the extent of the family's commitment and love there are some images that spring to mind now, as well as giving an indication of just how important it is to us to still maintain at least a veneer of ordinariness in an extraordinary situation. I can see Bella, now almost three years old, trying to 'help' Grandpa. Of course, she has never known him to be anything other than as he is really. That saddens me at times, because she will never know the man who was full of life and energy.*

165

She will never remember him holding her, being strong enough to put her on his lap while she had her bottle. She will not remember the joy in his eyes, or the smile on his face when she bounces into the room, so full of life, a smile he still tries to summon up even now. We must make sure, as she grows up, that we speak of him often, and show her the pictures and videos, so that she knows how much he loved her. On the night she was born, amidst all the drama of an arrival five and a half weeks before the expected date, and via an emergency caesarian section, when I arrived back home from the hospital to tell Keith we had a granddaughter – a much longed-for female addition to the very male household – was one of the only two occasions in this whole, long saga that left him with the ability to cry. But, back to her two and three quarter years present – how does she 'help' Grandpa? She is often here in the afternoons and around the 4 o'clock ritual of 'tea and tablets' Keith finds it impossible to manage whole tablets nowadays and we have found that the best way for him to take them is crushed up in yoghurt. Bella's 'helping' is to want to feed Grandpa with the yoghurt! I am sure that, as you read this, you can conjure up the images of what happens next! I make sure that the tablets have been taken before handing the spoon over to Bella then, as long as Keith is 'with it' enough that day, to go along with these well meant, loving efforts. Bella perches on the edge of Keith's chair, or sits on the bed to give him the rest of the yoghurt. Her aim is pretty accurate – most of the time! Her loving care never misses, however!

Jonathon, on the other hand, now 13 years old, is developing all the strength of a young man and can genuinely help out with lifting and moving Keith when we need him to do so. Alongside the strength, however, is a gentleness and compassion which move me to tears. He is not afraid to show his emotions, and when he arrives at the weekends, will go straight to Keith and hug him close. Today, for example, he was perched on the edge of Grandpa's chair, patiently trying to find out if he wanted a cup of tea. With his arm around Keith he repeated the question until some sort of answer came back. Then he made the tea and he and Michelle managed to get Keith to drink some of it. That may sound such a small thing in itself, but that *would have taken around 45 minutes in total and 45 minutes in the life of a teenager is no small gift!*

*Sadly, even Jonathon cannot really remember his Grandpa as anyone other than the person who constantly needs help. He cannot remember that it was Grandpa who often took him to nursery or collected him, who played cricket with him, or read him bedtime stories and, again, that saddens me. On the other hand, however, having to cope with Keith's illness, to confront the reality that he will not recover and that one day he will die, had helped to form his character and make him the compassionate young man he is today. His strong Christian faith grounds him and sustains him. To pray alongside Jonathon is to hear the voice of Jesus speaking. There is much to be grateful for in all this.*

*And then there is baby Noah. Born eight weeks prematurely on December 1ˢᵗ, 2009. Keith was very poorly indeed during November and December and at times I wondered if he would ever get to hold this newest addition to the Prestney family. Ben, Tonia and baby Noah finally made it to Lawford just after Christmas. Keith made a tremendous effort to get dressed and come downstairs to be there when they arrived and had the best couple of days he had had for weeks. Ben placed this little tiny baby in Keith's arms and those arms wrapped themselves round this precious bundle and he started to rock Noah gently, just as he had with his own sons. Noah, at first, crying loudly, became still and content and Keith even managed a soft 'hello' as he looked at him in his arms – a very emotional moment for us all. So precious was that time that Keith did not really want to let go!*

*Ben and Tonia have managed three more visits since then and, whenever they arrive with Noah, the transformation in Keith is remarkable. He is, I have to say, completely exhausted and often bedridden for a few days afterwards, but these times are so precious that it all seems worthwhile. Noah too, will only have pictures and videos to tell him of those times, but I think it will be important for him to know how much he was loved by his Grandpa.*

*Even the boys and their wives, Teresa and I try to protect the family, as far as we are able, from the more distressing parts of Keith's care,*

167

*although I have no doubt that any or all of them would gladly share that too. It is not just the physical care of taking Keith to the loo, or washing him, or cleaning him up, since he is now doubly incontinent, but the emotional and psychological battle that rages inside that I want to try to shield them from. Simon experienced this a couple of weeks ago when, in trying to help the relief carer to get Keith onto the stairlift and ready for bed, Keith 'disappeared' into himself and, not knowing who Simon was, lashed out at him. Fortunately, for Keith to actually hit out at any of us is rare and my heart goes out to those who deal daily with the violent aspects of dementia.*

*One day we may be there too, who knows where this wretched disease may take us all, but at least, at the moment, it is rare. However, it can often be a bit of a battle to get Keith dressed and undressed as he 'grabs' for his clothes or for us. His limbs are unyielding as we try to take off shirts or put on pyjamas and, coming at the end of a long day, for the carers and for me, can be exasperating at times.*

*Simon experienced, as a one-off event, what we experience daily and it really upset him. With two of us on hand, usually Teresa and me, we manage. If Keith gets too agitated with one of us, the other can usually step in to help and to bring Keith back to calmness.*

*What will happen, I wonder, if the time ever comes when we can not physically manage Keith? I truly pray that God will call Keith home before that time comes.*

*So, the family remain close, if perhaps shielded from the worst moments as is possible, but what of the wide family, of close friends, of acquaintances?*

Once Keith was in his chair, that was where he'd stay until someone helped him to move, which makes what happened in April 2010 all the more amazing. I could hardly believe my eyes when suddenly, unassisted, he rose to his feet and began to walk from the lounge towards the kitchen. I was flabbergasted – and shocked.

'Keith, what are you doing?' I cried as I hurried to his side, convinced he was about to fall. I took hold of his hand but he seemed determined to keep going. He was slowly heading towards the back door.

'Are you trying to go outside?' I asked.

Gently, he nodded his head. He'd been unable to leave the house at all for months and months so I was not about to try to stop him. What would be the worst thing that could happen? Maybe he'd have a fall but this was obviously something so important for him to do, who was I to stop him? We found ourselves in the garden. Slowly, slowly we wandered around, with Keith, despite being very wobbly, stopping regularly just to touch and smell the flowers and the leaves. Meanwhile, I was clinging firmly on to his other hand just in case he took a tumble.

After a few moments we headed back for the safety of the lounge. As we approached the back door Teresa arrived just in time to help me settle him comfortably in his chair. How on earth did Keith manage to do this? By the time he was back in his chair he was totally exhausted but, at least, I'm sure I now know why this little expedition was so very important to him – Keith had been determined to say a final farewell to the garden he loved. Outside was his world – with plants and trees – for just a short while, the man from the orchard was back where he belonged.

# A PEACEFUL FAREWELL

The following Monday, Keith was helped downstairs. We didn't know it at the time but this would be the final occasion he would be able to do so. He stayed for two or three hours but was so sleepy it was decided to take him back up to his bed. By this time Keith was probably sleeping 20 out of every 24 hours. It took a full 30 minutes to help him with his tablets. As Teresa and I left his bedroom, Teresa suggested what we should do with him the following day. For once, I disagreed with her. 'No Teresa, I don't think we can put him through any more. I think Keith is trying to show us he's had enough. If he doesn't want to get out of bed or to shower tomorrow, I think we should just let him rest.'

The next day Keith ate just a minimal amount and, that night, yet again, we had a terrible struggle trying to get his tablets down him. This time, however, we eventually realised is was not because Keith could not swallow them but because he'd just decided he no longer wanted to take them. It was as if he'd finally decided to give up his struggle. He'd had enough.

Keith had been unable to speak a single word all day. That night, I was the last person to leave his room and, as usual, I left him with the words 'Goodnight darling, God bless', and he'd always respond with 'Goodnight, I love you'. Yet, despite his incredible tiredness that night, those were the last words he ever whispered to me.

The following morning I went into his room with a glass of water and his tablets. I tried again to help him take his medication but such was his poor state, he began to choke on them. It was very frightening. Strange as this may seem, Keith's illness meant he took his morning tablets while still asleep. He couldn't open his eyes until he'd had them. This was a morning ritual. However, the crisis passed, although Keith still had not been able to swallow his medication.

Later in the day, Andrew's wife Kay had told me I looked so tired that I should go with her to the nearby town of Hadleigh with her and little Bella. I wasn't sure this would be such a good idea but, eventually, I decided to go. Teresa was just as capable as I was to

170

help Keith with his tablets. All the time I was in Hadleigh I was regularly phoning home to see how it was going with Keith. No joy, he was still fast asleep, no tablets had been administered. I just couldn't relax and decided to return home by late morning. As soon as I saw Keith I knew something had happened when I couldn't get any response at all from him. I telephoned Dr Bettle, Keith's GP. Within minutes he was at Keith's bedside.

'I think,' he said, 'this is the time to stop his medication.'

I telephoned the boys who hurried over to be with their father. The remnants of the last dosage of medication were still in Keith's system and he seemed so very peaceful. This would have been the ideal time for him to slip quietly away. But, then again, this is Keith we're talking about. He hadn't read the script!

As the effect of the medication wore off, Keith experienced pain if we tried to move him. His eyes would open wide and he'd appear terrified if he couldn't see me. All the hallucinations seemed to be coming back to haunt him. I couldn't bear to see him like this so I called back Dr Bettle. He arrived and administered a syringe driver which, over the next few days, the district nurses changed for Keith.

Had anyone suggested Keith would still be with us at the weekend we would have thought they were mad. But he was. How Keith could have survived so long without food and hardly any water amazed us all. Everyone was with us and the boys spent ages by Keith's bedside saying their goodbyes. It may sound strange, but it was absolutely beautiful in Keith's room. Even the district nurses were wondering 'why can't it always be like this?'

Basically, Keith was dying peacefully in his own bed, surrounded by everyone that loved him. Outside there was beautiful, sunny weather, the blossom was on all the trees, it just looked so wonderful when we looked out of the bedroom window and, as Andrew described the scene, 'it was a film-maker's dream – there was Dad, a dedicated apple grower surrounded at the end of his life by beautiful apple blossom'.

It was so peaceful and we had music playing in the background and little Bella playing at the foot of Keith's bed. At no time was Keith left alone, there was always someone with him.

171

Bella has a favourite book – *The Goodbye Boat* – which she found on one of my shelves several months previously. It's about a grandmother who died, a gentle child's story about the end of life. I decided this would be a good time to read it to her again. I explained that her grandpa was asleep but, this time, it was a very different kind of sleep. This time he wouldn't be waking up again. It was amazing to see how accepting Bella was of the situation. It was very moving to see her sitting on Keith's bed, totally unaware she was being watched, as she chatted away to her grandfather.

Monday morning arrived, so did Tuesday, as did Wednesday, then Thursday. Keith was still with us, unconscious, but with us just the same. However, it was obvious that his levels of unconsciousness were deepening all the time. Each day Dr Bettle would appear, and each day he could not believe that Keith was still hanging on.

It's strange how your thoughts can wander in times like this. I've always read a lot and the situation we now found ourselves in reminded me of a poem I'd read in a book by Sheila Cassidy. The book, entitled *Sharing the Darkness*, features a moving piece by Sidney Carter which seemed so relevant at this particular time:

*No revolution will come in time*
*to alter this man's life*
*except the one surprise*
*of being loved.*

*He has no interest in Civil Rights*
*Neo-marxism*
*psychiatry*
*or any kind of sex.*

*He has only twelve more hours to live so never mind*
*about a cure for cancer, smoking, leprosy*
*or osteoarthritis.*
*Over this dead loss to society*
*you pour your precious ointment,*

*call the bluff*
*and laugh at the*
*fat and clock faced gravity*
*of our economy.*

*You wash the feet that*
*will not walk tomorrow.*
*Come levity of love,*
*show him, show me*
*in this last step of time*
*Eternity, leaping and capering.*

Those words, particularly *'You wash the feet that will not walk tomorrow'* I find particularly moving and poignant.

Night after night I had been sitting next to Keith's bed, holding his hand and talking to him, trying to make the most of the little time we had left together. On the Friday though, Keith's kidneys eventually failed.

On Saturday, the family gathered once more at The Rectory, each of us taking turns to hold Keith's hand and to talk to him. How on earth had he been able to cling on to life for so long?

Simon used the opportunity of a private moment at his Dad's bedside to have a heart-to-heart chat: 'Naturally, I told Dad how much I loved him. Dad hadn't developed a faith until quite late in his life, so I talked to him about that. By this time I too had a deep faith so this was yet another bond Dad and I had formed. In a strange way, the deep bond between Dad and I had been even further improved because of his illness. I'd say that, as boys, we were probably closer to Mum than Dad, simply because he was always working so hard for such long hours. In a way, that caused him to miss out a lot as far as his children were concerned. The period of his illness, however, brought us all much closer to him than ever.'

Ben also said his goodbyes to his father when it had appeared the end was imminent. He'd spent time alone with Keith, sat next to him and said all he felt he had needed to say. He told Keith that he loved him, that he was proud of him but was not really sure his father would have taken any of it in.

As for Andrew, he'd already said a thousand goodbyes to his father so he chose instead just to sit in silence next to Keith's bed. 'I think we all grieved at different times and at a different pace,' he said. 'My grieving was done internally and usually after spending time with Dad when he'd had a bad day or when there had been a noticeable change in his motor or cognitive skills, particularly when he'd struggled to chew or swallow.'

That night, I sat with Keith when Jonathon walked into the room. 'Grandma,' he said, 'I'd been hoping to get you two on your own, am I intruding?' He was 13 years old, remember. 'Of course you're not,' I replied. 'That's good,' he said, 'would you mind if I prayed with you?'

The next day, Sunday, we experienced an incredible moment. Keith was still deeply, deeply unconscious when Simon and Michelle went next door for the church service. Several months previously, while I was ill, I had been in Chelmsford Cathedral and had learned a very moving religious song, the words of which are:

*I will wait for your peace to come*
*I will wait for your peace to come*
*And I'll sing in the darkness and I'll wait without fear*
*I will sing in the darkness and I'll wait without fear*

I'd taken this song back to our church and the choir had learned to sing and harmonise it beautifully.

While the service was under way, Teresa and I decided to bed bath Keith. We changed the sheets, his pyjamas and washed him from top to toe, even though he was deeply unconscious. Then there was a point while we were washing him that I thought Keith had died. 'Stop, Teresa, I think he's gone'.

At that very moment, the choir were singing *I will wait for your peace to come*. Simon and Michelle in the church were convinced at

174

this moment that Keith had passed away, it was, they said, as if everyone was holding their breath. Then, suddenly, Keith was back again. I'm convinced he'd briefly left his body and came back into it again. Teresa and I carried on with his bed bath.

Again, for days, Keith had not been left on his own at all. However, for just half an hour, while we all had Sunday lunch, we were all gathered around the table, taking turns to pop upstairs to be with him. While eating our dessert, I was sitting at the table, holding little Noah, when Teresa went up to check on Keith. Now, Teresa, although she doesn't broadcast it, is a deeply religious lady. She sat next to Keith's bed listening to a bible reading on her laptop. Hearing a sound, she turned towards Keith and was convinced he had just died. She hurried downstairs to tell us, 'Thanks be to God, Keith has gone'.

We all shot upstairs and stood around Keith as he took his final breaths. He slipped away so very peacefully, surrounded by his family as he would have wanted, having been unconscious for the past 12 days.

# 'GRANDPA'S GOODBYE PARTY'

Even now, I do not know how Keith kept going, except that, I think he understood particularly over that busy Easter period that I was so busy – it was almost as if he'd thought 'I'll hang on . . . I'll wait because I'll need her when the time comes'.

When people ask me if I'm grieving, well, of course I am. My husband of 40 years has gone and he's never coming back. I know one day I'll see him again, but he's never coming back here and that is a cause of great pain to me.

But his death was so beautiful, so peaceful, everything a death should be. There was laughter, there was joy, there were tears and a feeling of release. I realised I couldn't possibly ask for him to come back – not to that terrible illness.

We managed it – to keep Keith at the heart of his family – right to the very end of his life. Sink or swim, that's what they say. Well, that's what we, as a family, had to do for 11 years. There was no alternative but I'm so glad we did it.

The Rectory seemed so empty after Keith's passing. For the past few years our home had been shared with a succession of carers and cluttered up with various appliances to make Keith's life more bearable. But, surprisingly enough, I didn't feel any sense of loneliness at all. I'd thought it would be awful, terrible to come back into the house on my own. But, although it was empty and quiet, it was a beautiful house which seemed to wrap itself around you and take care of you.

I thought I'd hate to go upstairs again after Keith died but, the day he left the house at around 8pm that Sunday, Ben and his family stayed overnight. The rest of the family all met up again the following morning in the nearby village of Dedham and, that, to me, was the worst day as we were all grieving and were not knowing quite what to do.

We returned to The Rectory and there was chaos everywhere, Bella's toys all over the place, photographs all over the floor that Ben had been sorting through ready for Keith's funeral, and people popping in and out.

It was the one time I felt I couldn't cope – I can't be doing this. I didn't want anybody here with me any more. I needed to be by myself. Fortunately everyone seemed to realise how I was feeling and, one by one, they left me to adjust to life on my own but not before the boys had taken everything such as the hospital bed, the hoists, the slings and all the other paraphernalia out of the house. The room seemed so different without Keith's chair. In fact it's gone to a good home, we gave it to Marshall, the guy who kept the churchyard tidy, for his dad who, strangely enough, had just been diagnosed with Parkinsons Disease.

So, there I was, alone – apart from Teresa – in The Rectory and, immediately we just blitzed the house from top to bottom, in a sense, turning what had become a hospital, back into a home. It soon became obvious Teresa needed some time alone to cope with her grief and I didn't want my family around me because I was finding it difficult to cope with my own grief, let alone theirs.

When I finally dropped into my bed that night I felt totally at peace and, more importantly now, Keith was at peace too. It had been horrid to see what Keith had gone through, to see what he had lost. But, through all the sadness, I often admired that great patience of his, the tolerance he had. I just cannot work out how he did it. I could never have been that patient.

What a wonderful man he was. An amazing man, as Simon said in his eulogy 'a gentle man in every sense.' Keith was my rock and soulmate – but let's get everything in proportion – he was still, in fact, just a man!

As far as Bella was concerned, Keith's funeral was Grandpa's Goodbye Party. The church was packed with family members and Keith's former friends and colleagues, not to mention a large turnout from the village. A collection was made during the service, the proceeds of which were divided between the church and Diffuse Lewy Bodies.

Following the service there was a slide show of photographs of Keith throughout his life projected onto the church wall. This was organised by Ben who really wanted to make a contribution to the proceedings but, in his own words: 'I was too emotional to have stood up in church like Simon did – prior to Dad's funeral this was one of the ways I found myself able to deal with what had been going on.

'I looked at this as a project through a photographer's point of view and got out all the photos I had of Dad. I wanted to show the pictures that best showed Dad as he was. It wasn't a difficult task at all – it was lovely. The one thing we had almost forgotten was Dad's smile – we hadn't seen much of that for quite a while but, in all the photos I chose he had this lovely smile on his face.'

Each of the boys and the girls played an active part in the service but I'm not sure either of the other two boys could have stood up at the service and delivered such a moving eulogy as Simon managed. Jonathon too, added in his own words on behalf of the grandchildren. Keith's sister, Pippa, from Canada arrived for the funeral and that was really important because, until that point, I don't think she'd truly accepted Keith had died.

Keith's coffin had been returned to The Rectory the night before and young Jonathon acted as one of the pall bearers at his grandfather's funeral service which was really one of the most moving moments for me. Following the boys and Jonathon carrying the coffin I suddenly began to wonder if I could go through with the funeral. Would I be able to cope with all the emotion of the occasion? Yet I'd conducted so many funerals in this very church and had always been the one to try to reassure the mourners that their loved one would be going to a better place, that they were 'Going home, moving on through God's open door'.

I think Pippa realised how I was feeling and she gripped my hand. 'Come on, we can do this together'. Yet, when I stepped into the church, it was as though someone had wrapped me up in this warmth of love and I was truly uplifted by it. Gone was the sadness. I found myself smiling and determined to make the most of what was going to be a celebration of Keith's life.

The day before the funeral I'd returned to Greshams Farm with my good friend Mary Ward where Keith, many years before, had planted all the apple trees around the pond. They looked a picture when we arrived, laden with blossom. I explained the situation and asked the current owners if they would mind if I took a branch off each tree to put on the coffin of the man who planted them? They kindly agreed. We picked some apple blossom and brought it, with the branches, back to The Rectory where they were made into a beautiful spray to place on top of Keith's coffin. Keith was such a down to earth man, there's no way he would have wanted any grand gestures or elaborate floral tributes. He was an apple grower and this just seemed such an appropriate way to send him on his way.

We had apple blossom from every tree he'd planted, plus blossom from all the trees in our garden, the ones he'd been so determined to say goodbye to just a few days previously. Also, Kay had the lovely ideas of putting apple blossom in each of the immediate mourners' lapels and of giving each of our grandchildren a strawberry plant set in a Greshams Farm box – which may seem a strange idea to some people – but it was so right for the occasion and, after all, you do just what you need to do at a funeral, there's no set rules if you want to make the occasion as personal as possible to the deceased. The service itself was conducted by Gill Moore, a fellow priest from the parish and the Rev'd Paul Mann and Margaret Southgate our Lay Reader. It was not until we were outside by the graveside that I conducted The Commital.

So, Keith probably had the kind of funeral he would have wanted – surrounded by everyone who loved him – his family, friends and colleagues, apples, blossom and strawberries, with no fuss, nothing showy - just a plain and simple 'Goodbye Party'.

# MOVING ON

I once read a book called *Love and Let Go* and, in it, there was a reference to 'keening', a word I'd never heard before. Basically, the word keening was used in the book to describe a mother's grief-stricken wail when she held her young daughter who had just been killed in a road accident.

Keening is a wail that comes up from the pit of your stomach, through your chest and out of your mouth. There are no tears – just an enormous release of grief that you have absolutely no control over. It just goes on and on and on as you release all that bottled-up pain you've been carrying around with you. After Keith's death I tried desperately to hide my true feelings of grief for the sake of my family. I'd tried so hard to keep a smile on my face, but this pretence was costing me dearly – I was bottling up my true emotions.

It was only when I found myself on my own at home that something, maybe a memory, something I heard on TV, something a friend may have said, or something I'd read in a newspaper or magazine, would defy my desire to contain my feelings of utter despair as I found myself releasing this banshee-like wail – an almost primal scream.

This occurred, in my case, several times in the privacy of my own home. There was a huge anger in me, not at Keith's death but at grief itself, and this was my way of letting it go. There's a depth of sorrow in grief that caught me by surprise, an emptiness that I could not discuss with anyone else. This was utter grief, utter blackness. I was missing Keith and I knew there was absolutely nothing I could do to bring him back.

I could always feel within myself if I was about to experience another bout of keening. I'd think, 'no, no, not again', as it was totally overwhelming but, looking back, maybe it was a good thing because, without that release, how would I have coped? I haven't keened now for quite a while but who knows if it will ever happen again?

These feelings of blackness, of despair, prompted me to see a counsellor though, looking back, it was perhaps obvious why I'd been struggling to come to terms with my emotions, after all, within a couple of months of Keith dying, I'd made other life changing decisions such as retiring from the parish and moving house, away from several of my very dear friends. Too much had happened in my life, far too quickly.

I recall a dreadful period of time when my life just didn't feel worth living, my grief was almost overwhelming. It was Easter 2011 and, even though I have so much to live for – my family, especially my lovely grandchildren, and my many friends – I was in a really dark, dark place. When you feel that low you just cannot appreciate that what you have is worth living for – it just doesn't register. I remember going to bed – it was Easter Monday – and feeling that I didn't want to wake up in the morning. I have to admit I was so low that I'd considered ending it all but, thank God, I didn't follow up on those powerful urges. Even now I hate Bank Holidays – now I'm just going to make sure that every time one comes along that I have plenty of things to occupy my mind. Without doubt, my visits to consult with a counsellor paid dividends in the end. That's not to say I don't have bad days but now they are far less frequent than they were.

Even now I miss The Rectory dearly. It was an enormous wrench to leave. I have so many lovely memories of that home. Even, believe it or not, Keith's death. He was in this beautiful home, he couldn't have died in a more beautiful place, with those lovely trees just outside his window and surrounded by his friends and family.

A while back, on the anniversary of Keith's death, the family were altogether and, by sheer coincidence, Teresa arrived. It was lovely to see her again. We decided we'd all visit Keith's grave. As we stood around the headstone, we explained to Bella, who was now four years old, that this was the place we like to stand to remember Grandpa. We stood in silence, each with our own private thoughts of Keith.

Then I just said, 'Come on then, let's have one memory each!' and every single one of us instantly said, 'his laughter' or 'his smile'.

If someone were to ask me of my most treasured, lasting memory of Keith, it would be such a simple answer – laughter. In Simon's case, he jokes: 'Whenever I see a Yorkshire Pudding, I'll think of Dad!'

Andrew remembers the man who was 'the rock at the centre of our family – a man who never had to lay down the law, a man who had a quiet authority about him that earned him the respect he deserved.'

Life with Keith can be defined in two different eras – when he was well, and when he was ill.

I look back to when he was well, all the wonderful times we had when we were together, building our lives, Greshams, raising a family, our holidays and the happiness we shared. The farm's financial worries we experienced tend to fade into the background as the good times far outweighed the bad. As for the period Keith was so ill, it's the responsibility I remember most of all, having to think for two people all the time. We were robbed of our retirement. Now, when I see an older couple in the street and I can't help thinking 'that could have been us'.

The past few years have been a steep learning curve for my family and me. When I look back to the time of Keith's original diagnosis there was so much we, as a family, needed to know but attaining that knowledge was not always easy.

I'd like to see much more information made available so that people can anticipate the progression of the disease in order to keep one step ahead of it. As I've already mentioned, I discovered that by keeping myself as informed as possible on the likely progression of the disease I had far more chance of dealing with a problem as soon as it arose. It's no good waiting until it does, that's too late.

You need to put yourself in a position that, when you realise a situation is changing or worsening, you need to get help as soon as possible. For example, once you realise a person's mobility is becoming more limited you need to arrange to have a stair lift installed before it is actually needed.

I'd also like to reassure people who find themselves thrust into a situation where they have become carers that there is help out there if you know where to look – whether it be for financial advice or assistance to mobility and similar issues. Admittedly, in my role as a parish priest I was aware of certain aspects of help that were available as several of my parishioners were utilising these services already – in some cases I had even helped arrange those services on their behalf.

You'd be surprised how many services are accessible – getting in touch with your local council to see what is available is not a bad starting point. You also need to recognise a point of time when the burden of looking after someone is beginning to get too much for you. It's important to seek practical assistance well before you find yourself unable to cope. You need to bear in mind that, if you are too tired to properly provide the level of care required you are of no benefit to the person depending upon it.

Help is out there – so make sure you get it before it's too late. I have included a *Useful Contacts* section and a *Useful Information* section at the end of this book that I trust will be of help to anyone finding themselves standing where I was back in 1999.

Let's be honest, it seems like the end of the world when a serious diagnosis such as any form of dementia is made but, I hope our story shows that, with the combination of good family support, the right medication, and a positive mental attitude, it may sometimes be possible to extend the patient's life – and the quality of it.

I realise, of course, that we were fortunate that Keith was able to recover to the level he did and that such a turnaround of fortunes will not be possible for everyone but, when Keith was really poorly prior to Giles prescribing the Exelon/Sinemet combination, there was no way we could have imagined that Keith would recover sufficiently enough to be able to enjoy continental holidays, days out, his garden and his family – yet all this turned out to be possible and for that we must be forever thankful.

At last, I've begun to get used to the fact that Keith has gone. I look back now on how time has begun to heal the pain I felt shortly after his passing. Every year I had conducted an All Saints and All Soul's Day service at which bereaved relatives and acquaintances come to church to light a candle in memory of someone in their lives who has passed on. By October 2010 I'd retired but I still went to the service at Lawford church. I remember spending almost the entire day just crying and right up to the time I went to bed that evening. I was desperately sad.

I didn't go to the service at Lawford the following year as I'd joined the choir at my new local church. This time, however, there were no tears, none at all. Gone was the feeling that I couldn't cope any more. I guess I can say that I'm now at peace. It's been one hell of a ride but I believe I've now, at last, come through to the other side.

# USEFUL CONTACTS

*All information under this section was obtained from the websites mentioned and was accurate at the time of publication*

## Alzheimer's Society:

*Mailing address:*
Alzheimer's Society, Devon House, 58 St Katharine's Way, London E1W 1LB.

*Telephone:*
020 7423 3500.   *Helpline:* 0845 300 0336

*Email:* enquiries@alzheimers.org.uk

*Website:* www.alzheimers.org.uk

The Alzheimer's Society website offers advice on the following issues: What is dementia?; an A-Z of dementia; factsheets; types of dementia; progression of dementia; training and publications for health professionals; symptoms and diagnosis; memory worries; treatments; living with dementia; younger people with dementia; remaining independent; support networks; sharing experiences; everyday care; coping with caring; care services; legal and financial; relationships; local information.

## Dementia UK:

**A charitable organisation aimed at improving the lives of dementia sufferers and their carers.**

*Mailing address:*
Dementia UK, 6 Camden High Street, London NW1 0JH.

*Telephone:* 020 7874 7200

*Email:* info@dementiauk.org

*Website:* www.dementiauk.org

The Dementia UK website offers practical advice to carers of people with dementia. The website also has a link to Admiral Nurses who are specialist dementia nurses working in the community with families, carers and supporters of people with dementia. Admiral Nurses are supported by Dementia UK.

The Admiral Nurses weblink provides advice on the following issues: practical and emotional support to people affected by dementia; symptoms; what to do; available support for carers, family carers and people with dementia; and contact details of regional centres.

## United Carers:

**A network of carers.**

*Telephone:*
020 7874 7209

## Parkinson's UK:

**A confidential service. Free DVD entitled *Being There***

*Mailing address:*
Helpline, Parkinson's UK, 215 Vauxhall Bridge Road, London SW1V 1EJ.

*Telephone*
Parkinson's UK (free from landlines and most mobile networks) on 0808 800 0303. Open Monday-Friday 9am-8pm; Saturdays 10am-2pm.

*Email:* hello@parkinsons.org.uk

*Website:* www.parkinsons.org.uk

The Parkinson's website offers advice on the following issues: Treatments; day-to-day life; symptoms and signs; telling friends and family; talking to your doctor; employment and Parkinsons; just diagnosed?; a question and answer section; diet and exercise; driving and Parkinsons; benefits and grants advice; advice for carers; and a helpline.

# USEFUL INFORMATION

*All information under this section was accurate at the time of publication*

Remember, if you have recently found yourself in a situation where you are required to care for a person with a dementia-related illness, there are many places to turn to for support, not least the organisations under our Useful Contacts section. However, on a more practical basis you may need to acquire specialist equipment to care for your loved one. There are also certain legalities to adhere to. The following information may be useful to you.

If the person you are caring for has been diagnosed with a dementia-related illness and that person is a driver, the DVLA must be informed. Contact the Drivers Medical Unit, D6 DVLA, Longview Road, Swansea, SA99 1TU. Alternatively, you can telephone 0870 600 0301.

If you are a driver/carer you should be able to acquire a Blue Badge which is a special permit for easier public parking. Contact your local council offices for details.

If you are a carer for someone of the opposite sex you may well find difficulties in accessing public toilets. However, keys for disabled toilets will overcome this problem. These are obtainable at a cost of £3.50 from RADAR. Write to RADAR, 12 City Forum, 250 City Road, London EC1V 8AF or email radar@radar.org.uk

Need a wheelchair? Contact your local GP practice.

Incontinence pads may be obtained by contacting your local District Nurse Service.

Keep your costs down. Certain supplies are VAT exempt, including incontinence pads, wheelchairs and commodes.

# ACKNOWLEDGEMENTS

I owe an enormous debt of gratitude to Ivan Sage for the work he has put into this book and his gentle guidance through my memory banks to make it possible.

Without Andy, Simon and Ben and their wives Kay, Michelle and Antonia, I don't know how we would have got through the 11 years of Diffuse Lewy Body Disease. They have been wonderful sons throughout their lives and I am immensely proud of them. That love and pride extends to their children, J-J, Bella, Noah, Finn and Holly. Keith's sister, Pippa, was and is a constant source of strength and support.

Our principle carers, Lorraine, Caz and the beloved Teresa provided support for us far beyond the call of duty and I will always be indebted to them.

Our medical team, particularly our consultant Giles Elrington and our GP Vernon Bettle held us and helped us and I am sure gave Keith a quality of life far beyond anything we imagined.

Keith's friends Louis Thorp and David Butcher for their faithful visits and our friends Mary and Bob Ward for their continued support during Keith's illness and beyond.

Finally, to the church family at Lawford, to those special people within it who through their quiet loyalty and love enabled me to continue to minister as their Parish Priest through every situation.

**The Gift of Time** is co-written with former journalist and feature writer Ivan Sage. This is his sixth book.

Other titles by Ivan Sage:
*The Party's Over . . . Living Without Leah,* Robson Books
(updated and reprinted in paperback as *Leah Betts, the Legacy of Ecstasy,* Robson Books)
*Some Mother's Son - Picking up the Pieces after Murder,* New Millennium Publications
*Lawford Life,* IRS Publications
*Out of the Shadows,* John Blake
*Not Stupid,* John Blake